Prentice-Hall
Foundations of
Modern Organic Chemistry
Series

KENNETH L. RINEHART, JR., Editor

Volumes published or in preparation

Workbook supplement

D1213568

WORKBOOK SUPPLEMENT

Prentice-Hall
Foundations of
Modern Organic Chemistry
Series

KENNETH L. RINEHART, JR., Editor

ORGANIC NOMENCLATURE: A PROGRAMMED INTRODUCTION

James G. Traynham

Professor of Chemistry
Louisiana State University

PRENTICE-HALL, INC., ENGLEWOOD CLIFFS, NEW JERSEY

Printed in the United States of America
C-64081

PRENTICE-HALL INTERNATIONAL, INC., London
PRENTICE-HALL OF AUSTRALIA PTY. LTD., Sydney
PRENTICE-HALL OF CANADA, LTD., Toronto
PRENTICE-HALL OF INDIA (PRIVATE) LTD., New Delhi
PRENTICE-HALL OF JAPAN, INC., Tokyo

Current Printing (last digit):
10 9 8 7 6 5 4 3

To
Professor C. D. Hurd
and the late
Professor R. K. Summerbell
who, a long time ago at Northwestern University,
taught me the importance of nomenclature and
the importance of teaching undergraduates

Preface

The long, improbable-looking names of organic compounds are often a source of amusement and perhaps bewilderment to an uninitiated person glancing through a textbook or a chemical journal. Even brief instruction in organic chemistry usually provides enough familiarity to dissipate the amusement, but bewilderment may remain. This supplementary text is intended to help students of organic chemistry replace both the amusement and bewilderment over nomenclature with the genuine pleasure that accompanies competence and confidence.

A course in organic chemistry can be a cultural experience in the best liberal arts tradition, but, lamentable though it be in our science-oriented culture, few students take the course solely for that reason. All students who register for organic chemistry– whether chemistry major, pre-med, engineering major, pre-nursing or ag student—are expected to demonstrate some knowledge of the subject in their subsequent studies or professional activities. The emphasis on reactions, mechanisms, and descriptions of bonding will differ for different groups of students, but nomenclature is important to all. Each student, regardless of the professional ambitions which led him to the organic chemistry course, will be expected to be reasonably familiar with the naming of compounds. Such familiarity, quite aside from professional activities, can materially aid us in reading labels on the products we buy and in evaluating the boastful assertions of advertisers (who, among other things, distinguish aspirin and sodium acetylsalicylate with the clear intent of misleading the consumer).

To be most useful, however, nomenclature must be precise, just as all language is most useful when precise. Precision demands insistence on such seemingly small things as a change of a single letter in a name, or a one-word rather than a two-word name. In non-chemical associations, consider the different implications of Francis and Frances, or by mandate and man date. Although there are more organic compounds than we care to count, some with more than one acceptable and used name, learning their names is simplified sufficiently by a few rules. These rules have evolved over nearly a hundred years and are the result of careful study and agreement among chemists around the world. With only a few, generally untroubling manifestations of local flavor, the names used for organic compounds by chemists who speak quite different languages are the same. The rules which lead to these names are not always calculated to produce the shortest possible name; they are calculated to produce a completely unambiguous name. Many chemists develop and use what amount to nicknames for some frequently used compounds whose full names are cumbersome. These nicknames (or trivial names, as chemists prefer to call them) follow few rules and seldom need be learned by the beginning student. Even when the trivial name is used for convenience by chemists, the correct, full name generally must be included in any written report or publication to insure proper identification of the compound by readers. The emphasis in this supplementary text is on the names which follow the rules.

The IUPAC* system of nomenclature utilizes different styles for names. Two styles, functional class names and substitutive names, are in general use. Functional class names are restricted to compounds of relatively simple structure, incorporate a class name, and are often multiple-word names. Substitutive names, used for complex and simple structures with about equal ease, employ systematic endings (rather than class names) for names which most often are single-word names. Both styles are included in this text, with about equal emphasis.

The design of this material reflects the author's conviction about programmed learning of organic chemical nomenclature: It is likely to be most useful as a supplement to the conventional classroom instruction in organic chemistry rather than as a self-contained set of materials for completely independent study. It should be construed, in effect, as a guide for home study in connection with a course. It provides opportunity for focusing of attention on important details of nomenclature and for practice which the increasingly crowded classroom schedule does not permit. Chemical knowledge is expanding so rapidly that even the beginning courses are plagued by necessary choices among numerous essential aspects of the subject. Organic nomenclature is one such aspect that lends itself particularly well to individual study and practice, and a command of nomenclature facilitates the student's efforts to grasp the chemical behavior of compounds.

For most students, most of the material in a beginning course in organic chemistry is learned most readily if they rely on a lot of writing while studying. Repetitious reading alone can breed a familiarity that falsifies the degree of real understanding and comprehension. Writing structures, names, equations, and definitions while studying usually leads to learning in organic chemistry. Use of some programmed learning materials may help students to develop the practice of using a pencil while studying all aspects of the subject.

It is my hope that this study guide will lead students to do the homework they should be doing anyway and to remove one of the stumbling blocks to real pleasure for them in learning in organic chemistry.

JAMES G. TRAYNHAM

---

* International Union of Pure and Applied Chemistry, an international organization which, among other things, sponsors meetings for the exchange of new scientific information and establishes tables of atomic weights and rules of chemical nomenclature.

About the
Program Itself

The chapter divisions herein are based on classes of compounds, with separate treatment of aliphatic and aromatic compounds. Although the sequence of chapters may resemble those of some textbooks more than others, the material is not based on any textbook. It can be used equally well as a supplement to textbooks which treat aliphatic and aromatic compounds together as to those which treat them separately, by simple choice of the relevant chapters without regard to the actual sequence in the book. After Chapter 4, the chapters are virtually independent of each other. For example, the chapter on carboxylic acids and the one on aldehydes and ketones have been written so that they may be used in either order.

To keep the book small, the coverage is selective rather than exhaustive. Some persons (both students and professors) who have reviewed the manuscript have urged that the coverage be increased to include more practice examples and more classes of compounds. These suggestions have merit but must be compromised with the desire to keep the book small—and inexpensive. The classes of compounds which are included have been chosen to teach the key principles of IUPAC nomenclature. Several classes of compounds (for example, phenols and heterocyclics) are not included, but all principles necessary for naming most of these classes without further instruction are included. There are 461 items altogether, requiring 971 responses; students report that the total program requires an average of 14-15 hours working time. I use it one chapter at a time, as a supplement to classroom study, rather than as one long assignment.

The material in this book has been used in mimeographed form for over two years in organic chemistry classes at LSU and for a semester or so at several colleges. I am grateful for the cooperation of other professors who tested the material with their classes and reported on its effectiveness: Dr. W. R. Edwards (LSU), Mr. W. G. Hines (Aurora College, Aurora, Illinois), Miss Tena Schultz (Augustana College, Rock Island, Illinois), Mr. D. L. Neff (School of the Ozarks, Point Lookout, Missouri), and Dr. G. A. Knesel (Southeastern Louisiana College, Hammond, Louisiana). They all report that the study material is useful and effective. During the past year, I have depended on the programmed instruction material as complete replacement for previous extensive classroom instruction in nomenclature. Student achievements on the nomenclature portions of examinations have at least equalled previous ones. Perhaps the most convincing testimony, however, comes from the students themselves. Those who have used the material in first semester request it, even from a different professor, in second semester; and other students in a different section for which the material was not provided have, on learning about it from friends, asked for it. On course evaluation sheets recently completed by students at LSU, among their candid comments about the organic chemistry courses were praises for the programmed nomenclature material they had been using.

I particularly appreciate the helpful criticism of the mimeographed manuscript and the genuine encouragement which Professor Charles D. Hurd gave so generously. Because of his assistance, this book is nearer to being the impeccable guide to nomenclature which I have hoped for.

J. G. T.

Contents

1

ALKANES 1

2

NOMENCLATURE OF ALKYL GROUPS 10

3

NOMENCLATURE OF ALKENES 19

4

ALCOHOLS 31

5

ALKYNES   39

6

ETHERS   43

7

CARBOXYLIC ACIDS   47

8

ACID DERIVATIVES   54

9

ALDEHYDES AND KETONES   59

DIRECTIONS FOR USE OF THIS BOOK

To receive maximum benefits from this book, the student must actually write and check his responses during his study. The answer sheets for the chapter being studied should be removed from the book, covered with a card or a sheet of paper, and exposed, one answer at a time, to check a response which has just been written in the appropriate blank space. If an erroneous response has been written, the student should review the preceding portion of the chapter or, later in the program, refer to the summary of nomenclature rules in the Appendix before continuing.

1

Alkanes

Learning nomenclature as well as chemical behavior of organic compounds is greatly simplified when the compounds are divided into classes. Classification depends on the kinds of bonds between atoms. Perhaps the simplest class of organic compounds is the alkanes, compounds composed only of carbon and hydrogen with only single bonds between pairs of atoms. Alkanes may also be called hydrocarbons, a name which signals the combination of hydrogen and carbon. Hydrocarbon is a name indicating only the kinds of atoms present; alkane indicates not only the kind of atoms but also the kind of bonds which bind them together (only single bonds between pairs of atoms).

In stable organic compounds, the valence, or bonding capacity, of carbon is four, and the valence of hydrogen is one. The simplest alkane contains one carbon and four hydrogens and can be represented by the structural formula

$$
\begin{array}{c}
\text{H} \\
| \\
\text{H}-\text{C}-\text{H} \\
| \\
\text{H}
\end{array}
$$

An alkane containing two carbons can be represented by the structural formula

$$
\begin{array}{c}
\text{H}\quad\text{H} \\
|\quad\ | \\
\text{H}-\text{C}-\text{C}-\text{H} \\
|\quad\ | \\
\text{H}\quad\text{H}
\end{array}
$$

Note that both of these formulas indicate four bonds to each carbon and one bond to each hydrogen.

1. An alkane containing three carbons can be represented by the structural formula

_____ .

2. This formula indicates_____(number) bonds to each carbon and_____(number) to each hydrogen.

1

3. For convenience in writing, condensed structural formulas are most frequently used. The carbons are still written separately, but hydrogens bound to each carbon are not. Condensed structural formulas for alkanes containing one, two, and three carbons, respectively, are CH_4, CH_3-CH_3 and_____.

4. Note that the condensed structural formulas still indicate the correct valence for each atom. Counting each hydrogen as one, we find that the number of bonds indicated for each terminal carbon in $CH_3-CH_2-CH_3$ is_____(number) and for the center carbon is_____ (number).

To name compounds we use stems which signify the number of carbon atoms present in the group of atoms being named. The stem signifying one carbon atom is meth, that for two carbon atoms is eth, that for three carbon atoms is prop (rhymes with hope), and that for four carbons is but (rhymes with cute). The stem is combined with an ending characteristic of the class of compounds. The characteristic ending for alkanes is ane.

5. The name for CH_4 is methane, formed by combining the stem, _____, signifying one carbon atom and the ending, _____, indicating class of compound.

6. In similar fashion, CH_3-CH_3 is named_____ and $CH_3-CH_2-CH_3$ is named_____.

7. A condensed structural formula for a compound named butane is

_____.

Statements 8 through 20 are concerned with the formula

$$CH_3-CH_2-\underset{\underset{CH_3}{|}}{CH}-\underset{\underset{\underset{\underset{CH_3}{|}}{CH-CH_2-CH_3}}{|}}{CH}-CH_2-CH_3$$

8. Since this formula contains only carbons and hydrogens and has no multiple bonds between pairs of atoms, the kind of compound it represents is an_____.

9. Complex alkanes can be named by using the longest continuous chain of carbon atoms as the basis of the name. The longest continuous chain, or parent chain, of carbon atoms in the formula above contains_____ (number) carbon atoms.

10. Draw a continuous line through the carbon atoms in this longest continuous chain.

$$CH_3-CH_2-\underset{\underset{CH_3}{|}}{CH}-\underset{\underset{\underset{\underset{CH_3}{|}}{CH-CH_2-CH_3}}{|}}{CH}-CH_2-CH_3$$

11. Stems signifying more than four carbons in the group of atoms being named are mostly Greek (some Latin) in origin. For example, pent signifies 5; hex signifies 6; hept, 7; oct, 8;

2

and so on. The stem which signifies the number of carbon atoms in the longest continuous chain above is _____, and the alkane name for this chain is _____.

12. All the groups attached to the chain of carbon atoms through which the line was drawn in (10) are called substituents. There are _____ (number) substituents shown in the formula above.

13. Hydrocarbon substituents are named by adding yl to the stem which signifies the number of carbon atoms in that substituent. For example, meth, which always signifies _____ carbon atom, becomes _____; eth, which always signifies _____ carbon atoms, becomes _____; and alk, the general stem for a hydrocarbon grouping, becomes alkyl.

14. The names of the three substituents in the foregoing formula are _____, _____, and _____.

15. Whenever two or more of the substituents in a formula are alike, a prefix such as di (for 2) or tri (for 3) is added to the substituent name to indicate the correct multiplicity. For example, two methyl substituents will be designated not by methyl methyl, but by _____.

16. Substituent names precede the parent chain name as modifiers to make a single-word substitutive name. A partial name for the formula, which specifies all substituents as well as the parent chain, is _____.

17. A correct name, such as that given in (16), specifies the total number of carbon atoms in the formula and may be checked easily by comparison with the formula itself. The total number of carbon atoms shown in the formula is _____ (number); therefore the name must specify _____ (number) carbon atoms. The parent chain name specifies _____ (number) carbon atoms, and the substituent names specify _____ (number), _____ (number), and _____ (number) respectively. The name thus specifies a total of _____ (number) carbon atoms.

18. In a substitutive (IUPAC) name, the substituents are assigned the lower possible numbers designating positions along the parent chain. Each substituent must have a number. The numbers to be used for the substituents in this formula are ____, ____, and ____.

19. Numbers are set off from each other by commas and from the written part of the name by hyphens; each immediately precedes the particular substituent which it modifies. The complete name for the formula then is

_____.

20. Let us reexamine the name. The portion heptane refers to _____
_____.
The portions dimethyl and ethyl refer to _____ on the parent chain; there are _____ (number) substituents on this chain. The numbers designate _____
_____.
Whenever numbers occur together in a name, they are separated from each other by _____; all numbers are separated from the written portions of the name by _____.

The use of hyphens to separate numbers from each other, or commas to separate numbers from the other parts of the name, is incorrect.

21. Consider the formula

$$CH_3-\overset{\overset{\displaystyle CH_3}{|}}{CH}-\underset{\underset{\displaystyle CH_3-CH_2}{|}}{CH}-CH_2-\underset{\underset{\displaystyle CH_2-CH_3}{|}}{CH}-CH_2-CH_3$$

which is to be named. The basis for the name of this formula is the _____ chain of _____. This parent chain contains _____ carbons. The stem signifying this number of carbon atoms in a group is_____, and the alkane name for a group of this many carbons is_____. There are _____(number) substituents on the parent chain; these substituents are named _____ , _____, and _____.

22. Numbers indicate positions along the parent chain, and it is possible to number the chain from either end. One direction alone is usually correct, for the rule to be followed states that the substituents must have the smaller possible numbers. Numbering from the left in the formula above assigns to the substituents the positions ___, ___, and ___. Numbering from the other end of the parent chain would assign to the substituents the numbers ___, ___, and ___. Since we must use the smaller possible numbers, the correct position designations are ___, ___, and ___. Each substituent must have a number in the name; the number for the methyl group is ___, and the numbers for the ethyl groups are ___ and ___. When two or more numbers occur together in a name, they are separated from each other by_____, and numbers are separated from the other parts of a name by_____. Substituents may be cited in a name either in order of increasing complexity (CH_3- before CH_3-CH_2-) or in alphabetical order (ethyl before methyl). Either order is acceptable by IUPAC rules; Chemical Abstracts uses the alphabetical order for simplicity of indexing.

23. For the formula in (21), we are now ready to write a complete, substitutive name, which is _____.

24. The basis of the name for the formula

$$CH_3-\overset{\overset{\displaystyle CH_3}{|}}{CH}-CH_2-\underset{\underset{\displaystyle CH_3}{|}}{\overset{\overset{\displaystyle CH_3}{|}}{C}}-CH_3$$

is the chain containing_____(number) carbons. The alkane name for a group of this many carbons is_____, and the complete substitutive name for the liquid compound represented by the formula is _____.

25. The name for the liquid compound represented by the formula

$$CH_3-CH_2-CH_2-CH_2-\underset{\underset{\displaystyle CH_2-CH_3}{|}}{\overset{\overset{\displaystyle CH_3-CH_2-CH_2-CH_2-CH_2}{|}}{C}}-CH_2-CH_3$$

is _____.

26. A structural formula for 3,4-dimethyl-3-ethylhexane is

_____.

27. A structural formula for 2,4,5-trimethyloctane is

_____.

ISOMERS

Compounds which have the same molecular formula (which merely indicates the number and kinds of atoms present in each molecule) but different structural formulas are called isomers. For example,

$$CH_3-CH_2-CH_2-CH_3 \quad \text{and} \quad CH_3-\overset{\overset{\displaystyle CH_3}{|}}{CH}-CH_3$$

(both have the molecular formula C_4H_{10}) are isomers. The structural formulas are different: one shows a continuous chain of four carbon atoms, but the other shows a branched chain of four carbon atoms. The two structural formulas represent two different compounds with different physical and chemical properties.

28. Compounds which may be represented by the structural formulas

$$CH_3-CH_2-CH_2-CH_2-CH_2-CH_3 \quad \text{and} \quad CH_3-CH_2-\overset{\overset{\displaystyle CH_3}{|}}{CH}-CH_2-CH_3$$

have molecular formulas of _____ and _____, respectively, and are called _____.

29. There are three isomers of molecular formula C_5H_{12}. The three structural formulas are

_____, _____, and _____.

30. In each of these three structural formulas, the valence of carbon is _____, and the valence of hydrogen is _____.

31. The substitutive names of the three isomers in (29) are _____,
_____, and _____, respectively.

    Alkane isomers containing fewer than seven carbon atoms may also be differentiated by the use of structural prefixes. The IUPAC names of the unbranched isomers do not contain any structural prefixes, but prefixes are used for branched chain isomers. The structural prefix <u>iso</u> signifies a single carbon branch at one end of the parent chain. The prefix iso is not separated from the alkane portion of the name in any way in American usage.

32. There are two isomers with molecular formula C_4H_{10}. Butane is the IUPAC name for the isomer represented by the structural formula _____,
and isobutane is the name for the isomer represented by the structural formula

_____.

Note that the stem in both names (butane and isobutane) indicates the total number of carbons in the compound.

33. The stem to be used in the name for

$$CH_3-CH_2-\overset{\overset{\displaystyle CH_3}{|}}{C}H-CH_3$$

is _____, signifying a total of ____(number) carbon atoms. The appropriate structural prefix is _____, and the complete IUPAC name is _____.

34. The name for the compound represented by the formula $CH_3-CH_2-CH_2-CH_2-CH_2-CH_3$
is _____, and the name for its isomer,

$$CH_3-\overset{\overset{\displaystyle |}{CH}}{\underset{\underset{\displaystyle CH_3}{|}}{}}-CH_2-CH_2-CH_3$$

is _____.

35. The structural prefix iso is restricted to compounds with a single carbon branch at one end of the parent chain. No structural prefix is accepted to indicate the C_6H_{14} isomer with structural formula

$$CH_3-CH_2-\overset{\overset{\displaystyle |}{CH}}{\underset{\underset{\displaystyle CH_3}{|}}{}}-CH_2-CH_3$$

This isomer must be named as a substituted pentane and will be called

_____.

36. Two isomers with molecular formula C_5H_{12} are pentane and isopentane, whose structural formulas may be written, respectively,

_____ , and _____ .

37. A third isomer with molecular formula C_5H_{12} is known. By restricting ourselves to a valence of 4 for carbon and a valence of 1 for hydrogen, we can write only one other structural formula for C_5H_{12}. That formula is

_____ .

The names of C_5H_{12} and C_6H_{14} isomers which contain one carbon bonded only to other carbons contain the structural prefix neo. Like iso, neo is not separated from the alkane portion of the name in American usage.

38. The IUPAC name for the C_5H_{12} isomer described in (37) is _____ .

39. The IUPAC name for
$$CH_3-\underset{\underset{CH_3}{|}}{\overset{\overset{CH_3}{|}}{C}}-CH_2-CH_3 \text{ is} \underline{\hspace{3cm}}.$$

Isomers with more complex branching than that signified by the prefixes iso and neo, and alkanes containing more than six carbon atoms, are not named by use of structural prefixes. Names for these compounds are based on a substituted parent chain.

40. The IUPAC name for the compound represented by the structural formula

$$CH_3-\underset{\underset{CH_3}{|}}{CH}-\underset{\underset{CH_3}{|}}{\overset{\overset{CH_3}{|}}{C}}-CH_2-CH_2-CH_3$$

is _____ .

CYCLOALKANES

Cyclic hydrocarbons are named in much the same way as are acyclic ones. The operational prefix cyclo precedes the alkane name that would be used for a parent chain containing the same number of carbons as are present in the cycle or ring. Thus the formula represents a liquid hydrocarbon named cyclopentane. In American usage, the prefix cyclo is not underlined (italicized) or set off by a hyphen, although it is so treated by chemists in some other countries. For convenience, cycloalkanes are most frequently represented by geometric figures, such as

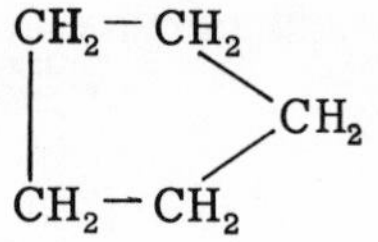

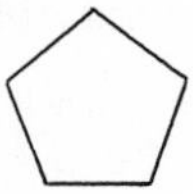

for cyclopentane. Such figures symbolize a carbon at each corner and as many hydrogens as are necessary to complete a valence of 4 for that carbon.

41. The symbol ☐ represents a compound whose molecular formula is _____ , whose

structural formula using C's and H's is

_____ ,

and whose name is _____ .

42. The symbol ⬡ represents a compound named _____ .

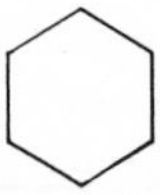

43. Substituents on the ring are treated just as substituents on a chain for naming purposes. Thus

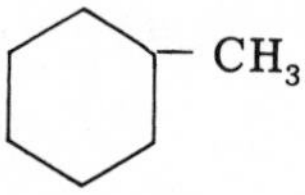

⬡ — CH₃

is named methylcyclohexane. The name of

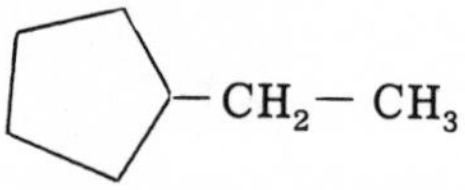

⬠ — CH₂ — CH₃

is _____ .

44. All of the positions in a cycloalkane ring are equivalent, and a number is not needed to indicate the position of substitution in monosubstituted rings. If there are two or more substituents, however, numbers are used to indicate positions of substitution. One of the sub-

stituents is always assigned position 1, and the smaller possible numbers are used for all others. For example, the name of

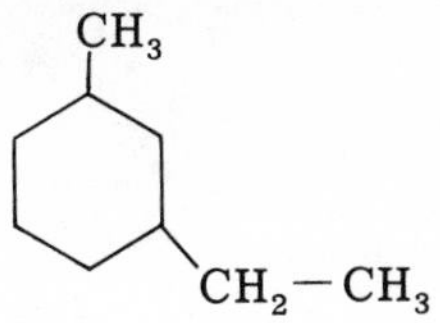

CH₃

CH₂—CH₃

is _____ .

45. The name of CH₃—⬦—CH₃ is _____ .

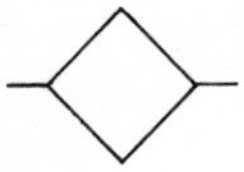

2
Nomenclature of Alkyl Groups

1. When an alkyl group contains only one carbon, it is designated a _____ group; when it contains two carbons, it is designated an _____ group. Methyl and ethyl are definitive terms, but definitive names for higher alkyl groups must differentiate isomers. Some isomeric alkyl groups containing fewer than seven carbons may be differentiated by the use of structural prefixes.

When all the carbons of the group are in a continuous chain and the attachment of the group (for example, to a parent alkane chain or to a halogen) is on a terminal carbon, the IUPAC name for that alkyl group uses no structural prefix. (The structural prefix n-, for normal, may be encountered in some common names which have the support only of frequent usage.)

2. The stem signifying four carbons in an alkyl group is _____, and the IUPAC name for the alkyl group represented by the formula $CH_3-CH_2-CH_2-CH_2-$ is _____.

3. The stem signifying five carbons in an alkyl group is _____, and the IUPAC name for the alkyl group represented by the formula $CH_3-CH_2-CH_2-CH_2-CH_2-$ is _____. An old name for $C_5H_{11}-$ is amyl; this name is still used by some chemists, but it is being abandoned in favor of the IUPAC name, pentyl.

An alkyl group whose point of attachment is a carbon bound to only one other carbon is classified as a primary alkyl group; one whose point of attachment is a carbon bound to two other carbons is a secondary alkyl group; and one whose point of attachment is a carbon bound to three other carbons is a tertiary alkyl group.

4. Butyl is the IUPAC name for the alkyl group represented by the structural formula _____; it is classified as a _____ alkyl group.

5. The alkyl group represented by the formula $CH_3-CH_2-CH-CH_2-CH_3$ is classified as a _____ alkyl group.

10

6. The alkyl group represented by the formula

$$CH_3-\underset{\underset{\displaystyle CH_3}{|}}{C}H-CH_2-$$

is classified as a _____ alkyl group, and its isomer

$$CH_3-\underset{\underset{\displaystyle CH_3}{|}}{\overset{|}{C}}-CH_3$$

is classified as a _____ alkyl group.

7. The alkyl group represented by the formula

$$CH_3-\underset{\underset{\displaystyle CH_3}{|}}{\overset{\overset{\displaystyle CH_3}{|}}{C}}-CH_2-$$

is classified as a _____ alkyl group.

The structural prefixes s- or sec- (for secondary-) and t- or tert- (for tertiary-) may be incorporated in a name to designate a specific secondary or tertiary alkyl group, respectively, if no isomeric alkyl groups of the same classification are possible. These prefixes are underlined to indicate italics and are separated from the rest of the name by hyphens.

8. The IUPAC name s-butyl or sec-butyl refers to the alkyl group represented by the structure _____. This is the only secondary butyl group which may be drawn.

9. There is a single tertiary butyl group, which may be represented by the structure

_____

and given the specific name _____ .

10. The alkyl group represented by the formula

$$CH_3-\underset{\underset{\displaystyle |}{|}}{\overset{\overset{\displaystyle CH_3}{|}}{C}}-CH_2-CH_3$$

is named _____ .

If the alkyl group has a single methyl branch at one end and the point of attachment at the other end, the structural prefix iso may be used. IUPAC usage of isoalkyl as a specific name is restricted to alkyl groups with fewer than 7 carbons. Similarly, the alkyl group related to the alkane neopentane may be named neopentyl. Notice that the prefixes s- and t- are underlined (for italics) and set off by hyphens, but the prefixes iso and neo are written without separation or underlining. This is an oddity of nomenclature that has little justification other than general usage.

11. Isobutane is the name for the alkane represented by the structural formula

_____

and isobutyl is the name of the alkyl group related to it. The isobutyl group may be represented by the structural formula

_____

and will be classified as a _____ alkyl group.

12. Isopentane may be represented by the structural formula

_____

and isopentyl by the structural formula

_____

The isopentyl group is classified as a _____ alkyl group.

13. $CH_3 - CH - CH_2 - CH_2 - CH_2 -$ is named _____ .
$\quad\quad\quad\quad |$
$\quad\quad\quad CH_3$

14. Neopentane may be represented by the structural formula

_____ ,

and neopentyl by the structural formula

_____.

15. The butyl groups for which the prefixes s- and iso are appropriate are often confused by students. The butyl group for which the prefix s- is correct contains a _____ chain of carbon atoms; the butyl group for which the prefix iso is correct contains a _____ chain of carbon atoms.

16. The name s-butyl designates the structure _____.

17. The name isobutyl designates the structure

_____.

18. Isobutyl is classified as a _____ alkyl group, and s-butyl is classified as a _____ alkyl group.

19. In a departure from strictly systematic nomenclature, the group

$$CH_3 - CH - CH_3$$
$$|$$

is named isopropyl instead of s-propyl. Some reasonableness can be associated with this name if the group is written as

$$CH_3 - CH -$$
$$|$$
$$CH_3$$

The group

$$CH_3 - CH - CH_3$$
$$|$$

will actually be classified as a _____ alkyl group, but its IUPAC name is

_____.

20. The compound represented by the formula

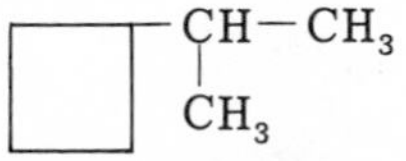

$$CH - CH_3$$
$$|$$
$$CH_3$$

may be named as a substituted cyclobutane. The name of the substituent is _____, and the name of the compound is _____.

21. The longest continuous chain of carbons in the formula

$$CH_3-CH-CH_2-CH_2-CH-CH_2-CH_2-CH_2-CH_2-CH_3$$
$$\quad\quad\ \ |\quad\quad\quad\quad\quad\ |$$
$$\quad\quad\ CH_3\quad\quad\quad\ CH_3-CH-CH_2-CH_3$$

contains_____(number) carbons. Two substituents named_____ and _____ are attached to the parent chain in positions numbered____and ___, respectively. The full name for the alkane is _____.

22. The alkane represented by the formula

$$CH_3-CH_2-CH_2-CH_2-CH_2-CH-CH_2-CH-CH_3$$
$$\quad\quad\quad\quad\quad\quad\quad\quad\quad\ |\quad\quad\quad\ |$$
$$\quad\quad\ CH_3-CH_2-CH_2-CH_2\quad\quad CH_3$$

contains a parent chain of_____(number) carbons and a substituent named_____. The substituent is located on position number_____, the name of the parent chain is _____, and the complete name for the alkane is _____.

Alkyl groups may be attached to atoms other than carbon; for example, a hydrogen in an alkane may be replaced by chlorine. These compounds may be named in two ways: functional class and substitutive names. Functional class names are usually two-word names formed by combining the name of the alkyl group with the class name of the compound. For example, CH_3Cl is a member of the class alkyl chlorides and is named with the functional class name, methyl chloride. For substitutive names, chlorine is regarded as a substituent (named chloro) on an alkane; CH_3-Cl is named chloromethane. Both names are acceptable IUPAC names, but functional class names are usually restricted to relatively uncomplex alkyl groups.

23. The functional class name for

$$CH_3-CH-CH_3$$
$$\quad\quad\ |$$
$$\quad\quad Cl$$

is _____, and the substitutive name is _____.

24. Isobutyl chloride may be represented by the structural formula

_____,

s-butyl chloride by the formula

_____,

and t-butyl chloride by the formula

_____.

25. Neopentyl chloride may be represented by the structural formula

_____

and named with the substitutive name, _____.
Neopentyl chloride is classified as a _____ alkyl chloride.

26. The substitutive name for

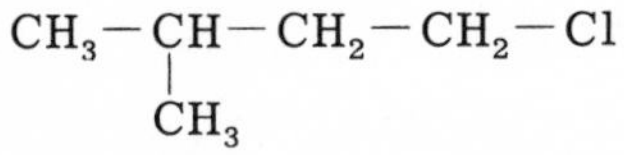

$$CH_3 - CH - CH_2 - CH_2 - Cl$$
$$\qquad | $$
$$\qquad CH_3$$

is _____; the functional class name for
this same compound is _____. This alkyl chloride
is classified as a _____ alkyl chloride.

27. The student should practice writing structural formulas from names of compounds. Consider the name 2,2,4-trimethylpentane. The parent chain name is _____ which signifies ____ (number) carbons in a continuous chain. Write a chain of C's to represent this portion of the name. _____ There are ____ (number) methyl substituents on the parent chain located at positions numbered ____, ____, and ____. Write the parent chain again, and number each of the positions.

_____

Now write the parent carbon chain, and place methyl groups in the proper positions.

_____.

Complete the formula by writing in H's to indicate the normal valence of 4 for each carbon.

_____ .

28. In the same fashion, step by step, write a formula for 2,4-dimethyl-3-chloro-3-isopropylheptane.

_____ .

29. There are three isomeric secondary alkyl chlorides with molecular formula $C_5H_{11}Cl$ which may be represented by the structural formulas:

_____   _____   _____

30. There are three isomeric tertiary alkyl chlorides with molecular formula $C_6H_{13}Cl$ which may be represented by the structural formulas:

_____   _____   _____

    Because of the possibility of isomers, we may not definitively name any of the secondary pentyl chlorides in frame 29 s-pentyl chloride nor any of the tertiary hexyl chlorides in frame 30 t-hexyl chloride. Each of the six alkyl chlorides in frames 29 and 30 may be named with a substitutive name.

31. A substitutive name for $CH_3-CH-CH-CH_3$ is _____ .
$$\qquad\qquad\qquad\qquad\quad\ \ |\quad\ |$$
$$\qquad\qquad\qquad\qquad\quad Cl\quad CH_3$$

32. 2-Chloro-2,3-dimethylbutane may be represented by the structural formula

_____.

Complex alkyl groups, and all those with more than six carbons, are named with substitutive names, not with structural prefixes. The position of attachment is always position number 1, and the longest continuous chain of carbons including position number 1 is chosen as the parent chain. For example, the secondary pentyl group

$$CH_3-CH_2-\overset{|}{C}H-CH_2-CH_3$$

is named 1-ethylpropyl (not 1-ethyl-1-propyl and not 3-pentyl).

33. The parent chain which is the basis of the substitutive name of the alkyl group

$$CH_3-\overset{|}{\underset{\underset{CH_3}{|}}{C}}H-CH_2-CH_2-\overset{|}{\underset{\underset{CH_2-CH_3}{|}}{C}}-CH_2-CH_3$$

contains_____ (number) carbons and _____(number) substituents. The name of this alkyl group is _____.

34. The compound represented by the formula

$$\overset{\displaystyle\bigcirc}{}-\overset{|}{\underset{\underset{\underset{CH_3}{|}}{CH-CH_3}}{C}}H-CH_2-CH_2-CH_3$$

may be named as a substituted cycloalkane. The alkyl substituent is named _____ and the compound is named

_____.

Parentheses around the name of a complex substituent may be necessary for complete clarity in a name; for example, (1-isopropylbutyl)cycloheptane.

35. 4-Chloro-6-(2-ethylbutyl)decane may be represented by the structural formula

_____.

17

36. The formula

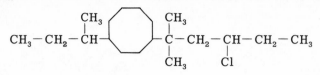

shows two substituents attached to a cyclooctane ring. The smaller substituent is named _____, and the larger one is named _____.
The two substituents may appear in the complete name in order of complexity or in alphabetical order; for a symmetrical parent ring such as cyclooctane, the first named substituent is assigned the smaller position number. The complete name for this substituted cyclooctane is _____.

SUBSTITUTIVE NAMES

Alkenes contain a double bond between a pair of carbon atoms, and the systematic ending to be used in names of alkenes is ene. The rules for naming alkanes apply to alkenes with two additional restrictions: The chain chosen as the basis for the name must contain the carbon-carbon double bond (the functional group), and the parent chain is numbered to assign the functional group the smaller possible number. The parent chain may or may not be the longest continuous chain of carbon atoms in the compound. The position of the functional group is designated by the lower number assigned to the carbons joined by the double bond; this number generally immediately precedes the stem of the name.

1. The parent chain in the compound

$$CH_3 - CH_2 - CH - C = CH - CH_3$$
$$\qquad\qquad\quad |\quad\ \ |$$
$$\qquad\quad CH_3\ \ CH_2 - CH_2 - CH_2 - CH_3$$

contains _____ carbon atoms.

2. The alkene name for this parent chain is _____ .

3. The substituent on the parent chain is named _____ .

4. When the parent chain is properly numbered, the functional group is assigned the position number ____ and the substituent is assigned the position number ____ .

5. The complete designation of the parent chain, including position of the functional group, is _____ .

6. The complete name for the formula is _____ .

7. The name for the parent chain in the formula

$$CH_3-\underset{\underset{CH_3}{|}}{\overset{\overset{CH_3}{|}}{C}}-CH_2-\underset{\overset{|}{CH_3}}{CH}-CH=CH_2$$

is _____.

8. The functional group is assigned position number____, and the substituents are assigned position numbers ____, ____, and ____.

9. Position numbers 2, 2, and 4 for the substituents are incorrect because_____
_____
_____
_____.

10. A complete name for the formula is_____.

11. The formulas for the isomeric alkenes containing four carbons are

_____, _____, and _____.

12. These formulas are named, respectively, _____, _____, and
_____.

    Cyclic alkenes are called <u>cycloalkenes</u>, and the alkene linkage is always assigned the number 1. The number is unnecessary in the name.

13. A structural formula for cyclopentene is _____.

14. A name for ⬡ is _____.

15. A structural formula for 4-<u>t</u>-butylcyclohexene is _____.

16. The compound named 1-s̲-butylcyclopentene may be represented by the formula

_____ .

17. Halogens and other substituents are treated exactly as they are in names for substituted alkanes. The name for $CH_2 = CH - CH_2 - Cl$ is _____ .

18. The compound represented by the formula

```
    ┌─── Cl
    │        CH₃
    │┃       │
    └─── CH₂ ─ CH ─ CH₃
```

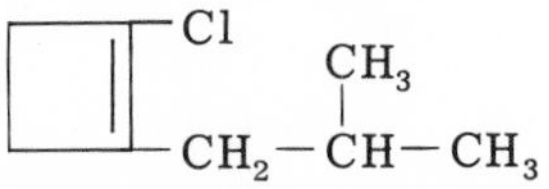

may be named _____ .

For the disubstituted cyclobutene illustrated above, either direction for numbering designates locations of the substituents with the numbers 1 and 2. When alternate directions of numbering produce different sets of numbers to designate locations of substituents, the alternate sets are compared term by term. The set with the lower number at the point of first difference in the two sets is the correct one.

19. Numbering of the ring in the formula

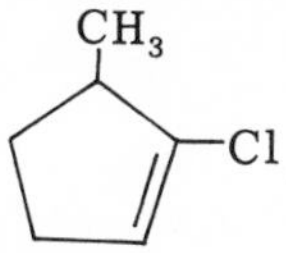

must assign numbers 1 and 2 to the carbons in the alkene linkage. If the carbon bound to chlorine is assigned position number 1, the two substituents will be located on positions numbered ____ and ____. If the other alkene carbon is assigned position number 1, the substituents will be on positions numbered ____ and ____. The two sets differ in the first number designating substituent position, and the set with the smaller first number designates positions ____ and ____. The correct substitutive name for the substituted cycloalkene is

_____ .

20. Substituent positions in the formula

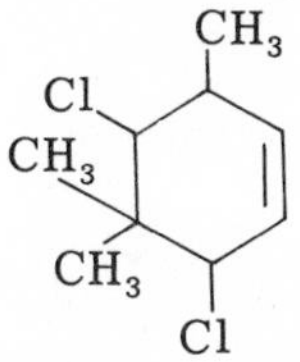

may be designated by alternate sets of numbers, which are _____ and
_____ . The two sets differ first in the third number, and the set with the smaller

third number is _____. The correct name for the compound represented by the formula is _____.

COMMON NAMES

A few low molecular weight alkenes of industrial importance are identified by common names, which are formed by adding the ending ylene to the appropriate stem. The alkene containing two carbons is named ethylene. Ethylene is actually retained as an IUPAC name, but no other alkylene names have such status.

21. The common name for $CH_2{=}CH{-}CH_3$ is _____.

22. The prefix iso designates a _____ carbon skeleton, and the name isobutylene refers to the formula _____.

23. Commonly used IUPAC names for the groups $CH_2{=}CH{-}CH_2{-}$ and $CH_2{=}CH{-}$ are allyl and vinyl, respectively. A functional class name for $CH_2{=}CH{-}CH_2{-}Cl$ is _____; a functional class name for $CH_2{=}CH{-}Cl$ is _____.

24. A structural formula for vinylcyclohexane is

_____.

25. A structural formula for allylcyclodecane is

_____.

GEOMETRICAL ISOMERS

26. The formulas for the isomeric alkenes containing four carbon atoms are

_____, _____, and _____.

Because of the restriction of rotation about a carbon-carbon double bond, some alkenes can exist as geometrical isomers. The distinction between these isomers depends on molecular geometry rather than on position of substituents or functional groups. The two atoms or groups attached to <u>each</u> carbon of the alkene linkage must be different for geometrical isomerism to be possible. That is, if one of the carbons is attached to two identical atoms or groups, geometrical isomerism will not be possible for that compound.

27. Of the alkenes represented by the formulas in frame 26, only _____ (number) can exhibit geometrical isomerism, namely _____ .

28. Formulas which reveal the geometrical isomerism of 2-butene are

_____ and _____ .

The adjectives <u>cis</u> and <u>trans</u> are used to differentiate geometrical isomers. Cis designates the isomer with like groups or atoms on the same side of the alkene linkage; trans designates the isomer with like groups or atoms on opposite sides of the alkene linkage.

29. The cis isomer of 2-butene may be represented by the formula

_____ .

30. The trans isomer of 1,2-dichloroethene may be represented by the formula

_____ .

The prefixes <u>cis-</u> and <u>trans-</u> are included in completely descriptive names of alkenes. These italicized prefixes are separated from the rest of the name by hyphens, and they immediately precede the number indicating position of the alkene linkage.

31. The completely descriptive name of

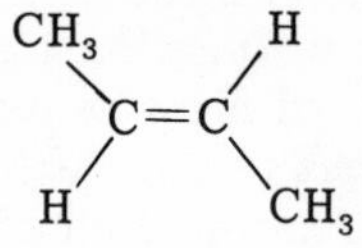

$$CH_3 \diagdown C = C \diagup H$$
$$H \diagup \qquad \diagdown CH_3$$

is _____ .

32. The prefix <u>trans</u>- specifies that _____

_____ .

33. A completely descriptive name for

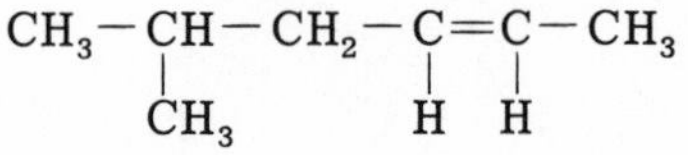

$$CH_3 - CH - CH_2 - C = C - CH_3$$
$$\qquad | \qquad\qquad\quad | \quad |$$
$$\qquad CH_3 \qquad\qquad H \quad H$$

is _____ .

34. A structural formula for 3,4-dichloro-9-methyl-<u>trans</u>-3-decene is

_____ .

Cycloalkenes with ring sizes smaller than 8 members have been prepared only as <u>cis</u>-cycloalkenes. Geometrical isomers of cycloalkenes with 8-membered rings and larger are known.

35. <u>cis</u>-Cyclooctene may be represented by the formula

_____

and <u>trans</u>-cyclooctene by the formula

_____ .

24

36. The geometry indicated by the formula

is _____ (cis or trans). The ring contains _____ (number) carbons, and a complete name for the formula is _____.

　　Disubstituted cycloalkanes also exhibit geometrical isomerism. The substituents can extend from the ring in the same general direction or in opposite directions, that is, the substituents can be on the same side of the ring (cis) or on opposite sides (trans). The prefix precedes the numbers and name of substituent to which it applies. For example, the formula

may be named trans-1,3-dichlorocyclobutane.

37. Consider the formula

The basis of its name will be the name of the ring, _____. There are ____ (number) substituents whose orientation, with respect to the plane of the ring, is _____ (cis or trans). These substituents are located on positions numbered ____ and ____. A complete name for the formula then is _____.

38. A structural formula for cis-1,3-diisopropylcyclopentane can be written easily when the name is considered by parts. The basis of the name is _____, whose formula may be written

_____.

The name specifies ____ (number) substituents which are named _____ and have the structural formula

_____.

These substituents are attached to the ring at positions____ and ____. The number 1 position of a ring will always be one to which a substituent is attached. The prefix, cis-, specifies that _____

_____

Combining the formulas for ring and substituents, with proper attention to position and geometry of substitution, one can write for cis-1,3-diisopropylcyclopentane the structural formula

_____.

39. A structural formula for trans-1-chloro-4-isobutylcyclohexane is

_____.

ALKENE ADDITION PRODUCTS: COMMON NAMES

Addition reactions are characteristic of alkenes. Several addition products are named with two-word names: the common name of the alkene from which the product was made is the first word, and a product class name (such as chloride, bromide, glycol, oxide) is the second word. For example, $Cl-CH_2-CH_2-Cl$ is commonly called ethylene chloride. Note that ethylene as a group (rather than an individual compound) has a valence of 2 and requires two chlorine atoms for ethylene chloride.

40. The name ethylene chloride reflects the fact that the compound named can be prepared if we add _____ to _____.

41. The common name of $CH_3-\underset{\underset{CH_3}{|}}{\overset{\overset{Cl}{|}}{C}}-\overset{\overset{Cl}{|}}{CH_2}$ is _____.

42. An IUPAC substitutive name for isobutylene chloride is

_____.

43. Methylene designates the bivalent group CH_2, and methylene iodide is a commonly used name for the compound represented by the formula _____.

44. Bivalent hydrocarbon groups containing only several CH_2 groups may be named by com-combining the appropriate multiplying prefix (tri, tetra, etc.) with methylene. For example, trimethylene is an acceptable name for the common divalent group $—CH_2—CH_2—CH_2—$, and trimethylene chloride is represented by the formula _____.

45. A commonly used classification for a compound containing two $—OH$ groups attached to different carbons is glycol. Like chloride, glycol may be used in a two-word name with common bivalent hydrocarbon group names such as ethylene. A functional class name for

$$\begin{array}{ccc} CH_3— & CH— & CH_2 \\ & | & | \\ & OH & OH \end{array}$$

is _____, and a functional class name for its isomer, $HO—CH_2—CH_2—CH_2—OH$, is _____.

46. A structural formula for isobutylene glycol is

_____,
and one for its isomer, tetramethylene glycol, is _____.

47. When $HO—Cl$ (hypochlorous acid) is added to an alkene, the classification name for the product is chlorohydrin. Ethylene chlorohydrin is the functional class name for the compound represented by the formula

_____,
and

$$\begin{array}{ccc} & OH & Cl \\ & | & | \\ CH_3— & CH— & CH_2 \end{array}$$

may be named with the similar name, _____.

48. If an oxygen atom is bound to two carbons to form a 3-membered ring, the compound may be called an alkylene oxide. For example,

$$\begin{array}{cc} CH_2—CH_2 \\ \diagdown \diagup \\ O \end{array}$$

is named ethylene oxide. The formula for propylene oxide may be drawn as

_____.

49. The functional class name for $CH_3-\overset{\displaystyle O}{\underset{\underset{\displaystyle CH_3}{|}}{C}}\overset{}{{-}\!\!{-}}CH_2$ is _____.

   The oxide group may be treated as a substituent named epoxy. Since it is a bivalent substituent, two numbers indicating the location of the epoxy substituent must be used in substitutive names.

50. The structural formula

$$CH_3-CH_2-CH\overset{}{\underset{\underset{\displaystyle O}{\diagdown\!\diagup}}{-}}CH-CH_2-CH_3$$

shows a substituent named _____ on the parent chain containing ___(number) carbons. The bivalent substituent is attached to carbons numbered ___ and ___. The complete substitutive name for the oxide is _____.

51. A substitutive name for the compound represented by the formula

$$Cl-CH_2-CH_2-CH\overset{}{\underset{\underset{\displaystyle O}{\diagdown\!\diagup}}{-}}CH-\underset{\underset{\displaystyle CH_3}{\underset{|}{CH-CH_2-CH_3}}}{CH}-CH_2-CH_2-CH_2-CH_3$$

is _____.

   Cycloalkene is used not only as the general parent portion of a substitutive name but also as the first word in a functional class name such as cyclohexene oxide. Additive names such as this one are permitted but discouraged by IUPAC rules.

52. The formula ⬡ may be named _____ and the name of ⬡O

is _____.

53. A formula for cyclobutene glycol is _____.

54. The formula   represents _____

and the formula   represents _____ .

DIENES

Hydrocarbons containing two separate carbon-carbon double bonds are named as alka-dienes. The appropriate stem signifying the number of carbon atoms in the parent chain is combined with the ending <u>adiene</u>. To learn why the "a" is included in the ending, try saying aloud "pentdiene" and "pentadiene." The "a" simply makes the word easier to pronounce. The parent chain is numbered to give the lower possible numbers to the double bonds; a position number for each double bond precedes the stem of the name.

55. 1,4-Pentadiene may be represented by the structural formula
_____, and its isomer, 1,3-pentadiene, by the
formula _____ .

56. The hydrocarbon represented by the formula $CH_2{=}CH{-}CH{=}CH_2$ is probably the most important diene from the standpoint of industrial use; it is named
_____ .

57. Isoprene is the common name (and an approved IUPAC name) for 2-methyl-1,3-buta-diene, which may be represented by the formula

_____ .
Isoprene is regarded as the building block for many complex compounds occurring in nature.

58. Propadiene, _____(structural formula), is better known as allene.

Allene is retained as an IUPAC name for this diene, but <u>Chemical Abstracts</u> uses al-lene and isoprene for the unsubstituted hydrocarbons only.

59. Allene has the structural formula _____. <u>Chemical Abstracts</u> names $CH_3{-}CH{=}C{=}CH_2$ _____ .

60. 1,3-Cyclohexadiene may be represented by the formula _____ .

1,2-Dienes are classified as cumulated dienes, 1,3-dienes as conjugated dienes, and dienes with greater separation of the two double bonds as isolated dienes.

61. Isoprene (2-methyl-1,3-butadiene) is classified as a _____ diene.

62. The hydrocarbon represented by the formula ⬡ is classified as a

_____ diene.

63. Allene, represented by the structural formula _____, is classified as a _____ diene.

64. 2-Chloro-5-ethyl-3,5-decadiene, represented by the structural formula

_____ ,

is classified as a _____ diene.

Hydrocarbons containing more than two separated carbon-carbon double bonds are named in similar fashion, "di" being replaced by the approriate multiplying prefix.

Alcohols

Alcohols are compounds in which an alkyl group is attached to an — OH group and may be represented by the general formula R—O—H (R is a convenient symbol for an unspecified alkyl group). Alcohols are named in three ways: IUPAC two-word functional class names, IUPAC one-word substitutive names, and, occasionally, one-word derived names. All three ways are used by chemists, with convenience in a particular situation dictating the choice among the possible correct names.

Functional class names of organic compounds are often two-word names. When the final portion of a name can stand alone as the name of an individual compound, modifiers (such as substituent names) must be written as part of the same word to avoid any ambiguity. When the final portion is a functional class name and cannot stand alone as the name of an individual compound, a two-word name is usually used.

Alcohol is a classification term, not the name of any individual compound, and it is treated in much the same fashion as other classification terms such as chloride and glycol. The name of the alkyl group attached to — OH is specified, and the name of the compound is completed by the separate word, alcohol. For example, CH_3— OH is methyl alcohol.

1. The functional class name for CH_3—CH—CH_3 is _____.
$\qquad\qquad\qquad\qquad\qquad\qquad\quad$ |
$\qquad\qquad\qquad\qquad\qquad\qquad\quad$ OH

2. The condensed structural formula for s-butyl alcohol is

_____.

3. Functional class names of alcohols are two-word names because _____
_____.

4. The name for the group

$$CH_3—CH—CH_2—CH_2—$$
$$\quad\quad\ |$$
$$\quad\quad CH_3$$

is _____ and the functional class name for the compound represented by the formula

$$CH_3-CH-CH_2-CH_2-OH$$
$$|$$
$$CH_3$$

is _____.

5. The common IUPAC name for the group $CH_2=CH-CH_2-$ is _____, and the functional class name for $CH_2=CH-CH_2-OH$ is _____.

6. The condensed structural formula for t-butyl alcohol is

_____.

Like alkyl chlorides, alcohols can be classified as primary, secondary, and tertiary.

7. Ethyl alcohol, represented by the condensed structural formula _____, is classified as a _____ alcohol.

8. Isobutyl alcohol, represented by the condensed structural formula

_____,

is classified as a _____ alcohol.

9. Allyl alcohol is a _____ alcohol.

10. These three alcohols are all primary alcohols because _____
_____
_____.

11. Isopropyl alcohol is classified as a _____ alcohol.

12. A secondary alcohol whose molecular formula is C_4H_9OH has the structural formula

_____

and the common (functional class) name _____.

32

13. There are three secondary alcohols with molecular formula $C_5H_{11}OH$; their structural formulas are

_____ , _____ , _____ .

14. The tertiary alcohol of lowest molecular weight has the structural formula

_____

and the functional class name _____ .

SUBSTITUTIVE NAMES

The rules learned for alkenes are followed for alcohols. The longest continuous chain of carbon atoms containing the functional group (OH in this case) serves as the basis of the name. The carbon to which the OH group is attached is assigned the smaller possible number. The <u>ending</u> which signifies alcohol or OH group is <u>ol</u>. This systematic ending is appended to the one-word IUPAC name of the alkane (minus the final e) corresponding to the parent chain. For example, the IUPAC substitutive name for

$$CH_3 - \underset{\underset{\displaystyle OH}{|}}{CH} - CH_3$$

is 2-propanol. Some chemists prefer to place the number closer to the functional group to which the number refers: propanol-2 or propan-2-ol. Although these styles are acceptable, most chemists, particularly American chemists, use 2-propanol.

15. The IUPAC substitutive name for $CH_3 - CH_2 - \underset{\underset{\displaystyle OH}{|}}{CH} - CH_2 - CH_3$ is _____ .

16. The condensed structural formula for 2-butanol is _____ .

17. The substitutive name for (cyclohexane with OH) is _____ .

Substituents are named and numbered as in other IUPAC names. Remember that the OH group is assigned the lower possible number.

18. The substitutive name for $CH_3-\overset{\displaystyle |}{\underset{\displaystyle OH}{CH}}-\overset{\displaystyle |}{\underset{\displaystyle CH_3}{CH}}-CH_3$ is _____.

A complex structural formula can usually be named rather easily in steps. Consider the formula

$$CH_3-CH_2-\overset{\displaystyle \overset{Cl}{|}}{CH}-\overset{\displaystyle \overset{CH_3}{|}}{\underset{\displaystyle \underset{OH}{|}}{C}}-CH_2-\overset{\displaystyle \underset{\displaystyle \underset{CH_3}{|}}{\underset{CH-CH_3}{|}}}{CH}-CH_2-CH_2-CH_3$$

19. The longest continuous chain of carbon atoms containing the functional group which will serve as the basis of the name contains____(number) carbon atoms. The IUPAC name for an alkane containing this number of carbon atoms is_____.

20. The IUPAC substitutive name for an alcohol with this many carbon atoms is

_____.

21. When the parent chain is properly numbered, the OH group will be on the carbon atom numbered____. Therefore, the parent compound name, including number, will be

_____.

22. There are____(number) substituents on the parent chain (besides the functional group); these substituents are named _____, _____, and _____; they are located on carbons numbered ___, ___, and ____, respectively.

23. As in all IUPAC names, the numbers are separated from the written parts of the name by _____ (and from each other, if necessary, by _____).

24. The complete IUPAC name for the complex formula above then becomes

_____.

25. This compound can be classified as a _____ alcohol.

26. Because the formula contains a Cl and an OH on adjacent carbons, the compound could be classified by the class name _____.

27. Chlorohydrins can be prepared by adding _____
to _____. The chlorohydrin above could have been prepared by adding _____to

_____(structural formula).

DERIVED NAMES (CARBINOL NAMES)

Alcohols are still occasionally named as derivatives of <u>carbinol</u>, a name synonymous with methanol, although carbinol names are not part of the IUPAC system. The common names of substituents on the carbinol carbon are specified, and, because carbinol is the name of a specific compound rather than a class of compounds, the complete name is a single word. For example, another name for <u>t</u>-butyl alcohol is trimethylcarbinol. It is convenient to draw a rectangle around the OH group and the carbon to which it is attached, that is, around <u>carbinol</u>. The substituents are clearly visible and are named in order of increasing size or alphabetically.

28. The alcohol whose IUPAC name is 3-ethyl-3-pentanol has the structural formula

_____

and the carbinol name _____ .

29. A carbinol name for

is _____. Another derived name, based on methanol, for the same alcohol is _____ .

30. The carbinol name for

$$CH_3-CH-CH_2-CH_3$$
$$CH_3-CH_2-C-CH_2-CH_3$$
$$OH$$

is _____. The IUPAC substitutive name for this compound is _____. The compound would be classified as a _____ alcohol.

ALCOHOLS WITH TWO OR MORE FUNCTIONAL GROUPS

Some alcohols contain two or more OH groups. Names for these compounds simply include a number indicating location of each OH group and the appropriate ending <u>diol</u>, <u>triol</u>, <u>tetrol</u>, etc. For example, ethylene glycol $HO-CH_2-CH_2-OH$, may be named 1,2-ethanediol. Note that the final "e" of the alkane portion of the name is retained for <u>alkanediol</u> but is omitted for <u>alkanol</u>. In general, the final "e" is retained with systematic endings beginning with consonants, and dropped with those beginning with vowels.

31. Isobutylene glycol, which may be represented by the structural formula

_____ ,

has the IUPAC substitutive name _____ .

32. The parent chain in the formula

$$CH_3-\overset{\underset{\displaystyle OH}{|}}{CH}-CH_2-\overset{\underset{\displaystyle OH}{|}}{CH}-\overset{\underset{\displaystyle CH_3}{|}}{CH}-\overset{\overset{\displaystyle CH_3}{|}}{\underset{\underset{\displaystyle CH_3}{|}}{C}}-CH_3$$

is numbered so that the OH groups are assigned positions____ and ____. The rule dictating the direction of numbering requires that the OH groups be assigned the
_____ numbers. The IUPAC name for the alcohol represented by this formula is _____ .

IUPAC substitutive names of unsaturated alcohols are formed by using <u>alkenol</u> rather than alkanol as the basis of the name. The position of the OH group is assigned the lower possible number. In cycloalkenols, the OH group is always on the number 1 carbon. No number designation is necessary for it in the name, but the number 1 is usually included anyway. The number designating the location of the alkene linkage generally precedes the <u>alken</u> portion of the name, and the number designating the position of the OH group immediately precedes <u>ol</u>. For example,

$$CH_3-CH{=}CH-\overset{\underset{\displaystyle OH}{|}}{CH}-CH_3$$

is named 3-penten-2-ol.

33. The structural formula for allyl alcohol is_____, and the substitutive name for allyl alcohol is _____ .

34. A structural formula for 2-cyclohexen-1-ol is _____ .

35. A substitutive name for (octagon)—OH is _____ .

36. The chain of carbon atoms which will serve as the basis of the IUPAC substitutive name of

36

$$CH_3-\underset{\underset{\underset{CH_3}{|}}{\underset{CH_2}{|}}}{\overset{\overset{CH_3}{|}}{C}}=CH-\underset{\underset{CH_3}{|}}{CH}-\underset{\overset{OH}{|}}{CH}-CH_2-CH_3$$

contains____(number) carbons, and the portion of the name used to designate that chain together with the functional groups is_____. When the carbon chain is properly numbered, the OH group will be on carbon numbered ____, and the alkene linkage will be assigned position number____. The basis for the name then becomes _____.
There are____(number) substituents (not including the OH group) on the parent chain. They are named_____ and _____ and are located on carbons numbered____and ____, respectively. The complete IUPAC substitutive name for the unsaturated alcohol becomes _____.

37. A structural formula for 5-chloro-3-methyl-3-hexen-2-ol is

_____.

38. A substitutive name for $CH_3-\underset{\underset{OH}{|}}{CH}-CH=CH-\underset{\overset{OH}{|}}{CH}-\underset{\overset{CH_3}{|}}{CH}-CH_3$ is _____.

39. A substitutive name for $CH_3-CH_2-\overset{\overset{CH_3}{|}}{CH}-$ ⬡ $-OH$ is

_____.

Unsaturated alcohols and cyclic alcohols, like other alkenes and disubstituted cycloalkanes, may exist as geometrical isomers. The prefix cis- or trans- precedes the number(s) modifying the functional group(s) to which the geometrical tag applies.

40. A structural formula for 2-methyl-trans-3-penten-2-ol is

_____.

41. A completely descriptive name, including identification of geometrical isomerism, for the compound represented by the formula

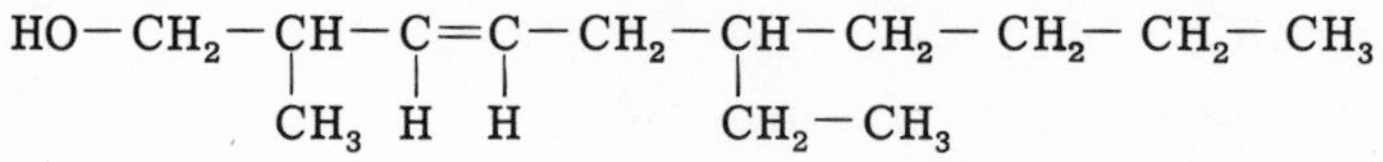

$$HO-CH_2-\underset{\underset{CH_3}{|}}{CH}-\underset{\underset{H}{|}}{C}=\underset{\underset{H}{|}}{C}-CH_2-\underset{\underset{CH_2-CH_3}{|}}{CH}-CH_2-CH_2-CH_2-CH_3$$

is_____.

Three convenient representations are used in structural formulas intended to show geometrical isomerism of cyclic compounds: (1) Perspective formulas with bonds above and below the plane of the ring. (2) A dark wedge representing a bond projecting out from the plane of the paper (plane of the molecule) and a dashed line representing a bond projecting behind that plane. (3) Dark dots representing hydrogens projecting up from the plane of the paper (plane of the molecule). Examples of these representations are shown here.

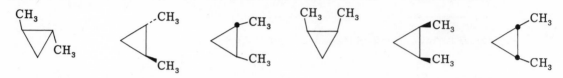

trans-1,2-dimethylcyclopropane   cis-1,2-dimethylcyclopropane

42. Convenient structural formula representations of cis-1,3-cyclobutanediol are

_____.

43. The formula for a vinyl group is_____, and a structural formula for trans-2-vinylcyclohexanol is

_____.

38

Alkynes contain a triple bond between a pair of carbon atoms somewhere in the molecule. They are named in two ways: IUPAC and derived names.

IUPAC NAMES

Alkynes are named in much the same way as alkenes. The systematic ending is <u>yne</u>, signifying the triple bond between a pair of carbon atoms. As the basis of the name, this functional group is contained in the parent chain, and its position is indicated by the smaller possible number, which generally precedes the stem of the name.

1. An IUPAC name for $HC \equiv CH$ is ethyne, and the IUPAC name for $CH_3 - C \equiv CH$ is _____.

2. In the formula

$$CH_3 - \underset{\underset{CH_3}{|}}{CH} - C \equiv C - \underset{\underset{CH_2 - CH_3}{|}}{CH} - CH_2 - CH_3$$

the longest continuous chain containing the functional group, $C \equiv C$, contains ____(number) carbons; the stem signifying this number of carbons is _____. The ending signifying the functional group, $C \equiv C$, is _____, and the name for the chain containing this group is _____. When the chain is properly numbered, the functional group will be assigned position number ____, and the parent name, including number, will be _____. The two substituents, named _____ and _____, are on positions ____ and ____, respectively, and the full name for the compound represented by the formula is

_____.

3. The IUPAC name for $CH_3 - C \equiv C - CH_3$ is _____.

4. The structural formula for 3-hexyne is _____.

5. The structural formula for 1-chloro-4-<u>s</u>-butyl-2-octyne will contain a parent chain of ____(number) carbons, signified by the stem _____. The ending, yne, indicates the functional group _____. The parent chain can then be written _____. The

substituent on position 1 is represented by the symbol _____, the one on position 4 by

_____.

The complete structural formula for 1-chloro-4-s-butyl-2-octyne may be drawn

_____.

DERIVED NAMES

The common name for ethyne is acetylene, and a number of simple alkynes are often named as derivatives of acetylene. For example, propyne may also be named <u>methylacety-lene</u>. If the alkyl groups attached to the acetylene unit have common names, the derived name is easily formulated. It may be convenient to draw a rectangle around the acetylene unit; the alkyl groups then stand out clearly for naming. For example $CH_3 \boxed{-C \equiv CH}$ is methyl-acetylene. Note that only one alkyl group may be attached to each carbon in the acetylene unit, and no indication of positions of the substituent alkyl groups is necessary.

6. The derived name for $CH_3 - CH_2 - C \equiv CH$ is_____, and the derived name for $CH_3 - CH_2 - C \equiv C - CH_2 - CH_3$ is _____.

7. Derived names are written as single words because _____
_____.

8. The structural formula of methylisobutylacetylene will show two substituents bound to the functional group, _____. The two substituents are named _____ and _____ and are represented by the formulas

_____   _____

respectively. The structural formula of methylisobutylacetylene may be written

_____.

9. The IUPAC substitutive name for methylisobutylacetylene is _____.

40

10. The common name for the group $CH_2\!=\!CH-$ is _____, and the derived name for $CH_2\!=\!CH-C\!\equiv\!CH$ is _____.

11. The derived name for $CH_3-\underset{\underset{\displaystyle CH_3}{|}}{CH}-C\!\equiv\!C-CH\!=\!CH_2$ is

_____.

   IUPAC substitutive names for compounds containing both a carbon–carbon double bond and a carbon–carbon triple bond are based on the general parent name "alkenyne." The parent chain is numbered so as to use the lower possible position numbers for the double and triple bonds. However, the double bond is given the preference if there is a choice, even though "yne" is the final suffix of the name. For example, $CH_2\!=\!CH-CH_2-C\!\equiv\!CH$ is named 1-penten-4-yne (rather than 4-penten-1-yne), but $CH_3-CH\!=\!CH-C\!\equiv\!CH$ is named 3-penten-1-yne. As these examples illustrate, the position number for the "ene" linkage generally precedes the stem of the name, and that for the "yne" linkage immediately precedes "yne" in the name.

12. Vinylacetylene, represented by the formula _____, may also be named by the IUPAC substitutive name _____.

13. Allylacetylene, represented by the formula _____, may be named by the IUPAC substitutive name _____.

14. The IUPAC substitutive name for the compound represented by the formula

$$CH_3-C\!\equiv\!C-\underset{\underset{\displaystyle Cl}{|}}{CH}-CH_2-CH\!=\!\underset{\underset{\displaystyle \overset{\displaystyle CH_3-CH-CH_3}{|}}{}}{C}-CH_2-CH_3$$

is _____.

   Compounds containing both an acetylene unit and an OH group may be named in a manner parallel to that used for alkenols. That is, such compounds may be called alkynols.

15. Remember that, for alkenols, the lower possible number indicating position of functional group is assigned to the _____ group, not to the _____ group. The number indicating location of the alkene linkage appears in the name before the stem of the name, and the number indicating location of the OH group appears just before the systematic ending _____.

16. The IUPAC substitutive name for $CH_2\!=\!CH-CH_2-\underset{\underset{\displaystyle OH}{|}}{CH}-CH_3$ is

_____.

17. The IUPAC substitutive name for $HC\!\equiv\!C-CH_2-\underset{\underset{\displaystyle OH}{|}}{CH}-CH_3$ is _____.

18. Oblivon, a hypnotic, is 3-methyl-1-pentyn-3-ol, which may be represented by the formula

_____ .

The group HC≡C— is often regarded as a substituent and is designated <u>ethynyl</u>. The ethynyl group is treated like any other substituent in names of compounds.

19. The compound represented by the structural formula

$$\underset{\underset{HC\equiv C}{|}}{\overset{\overset{OH}{|}}{CH_3-CH_2-CH-CH_2-CH-}}\underset{\underset{CH_3}{|}}{\overset{\overset{CH_3}{|}}{C}}-CH_2-CH_3$$

may be named as an alcohol, the group HC≡C— being treated as a substituent named
_____. The parent chain contains____(number) carbons. Since the functional group, OH, will serve as the basis of the name (compound being named as an alcohol), it will be assigned position number____. The three substituents will be on positions numbered____, ____, and____. The complete IUPAC substitutive name for the alcohol represented by the formula above is_____.

20. A structural formula for 1-ethynyl-1-cyclohexanol is

_____ .

Compounds having two alkyl groups attached to an oxygen atom are classified as ethers. Ethers are named by functional class names and by substitutive names.

FUNCTIONAL CLASS NAMES

Ether is a class name, not the name of any individual member of the class. Names ending in ether are therefore multiple-word names, not single-word names. Each alkyl group attached to the ether oxygen is specified by a separate word, and the name is completed by ether, also a separate word. The final word ether implies two alkyl groups; when the two alkyl groups are alike, the name of the group need be specified only once. Some chemists use the multiplying prefix di, but it is unnecessary (in the same sense that disodium sulfate includes an unnecessary prefix).

1. The functional class name for $CH_3-O-CH_2-CH_3$ is _____.

2. The functional class name for $CH_3-CH_2-O-CH_2-CH_3$ is _____.

3. A structural formula for methyl t-butyl ether is

_____.

4. The structural formula for the alkyl group vinyl is _____, and the structural formula for methyl vinyl ether is _____.

5. The stem indicating five carbons in a group is _____, and the name for

$$CH_3-\underset{\underset{CH_3}{|}}{CH}-CH_2-CH_2-$$

is _____. The common name for the group $CH_2{=}CH-CH_2-$ is _____, and the functional class name for the ether

$$CH_3-CH-CH_2-CH_2-O-CH_2-CH=CH_2$$
$$\overset{|}{CH_3}$$

is _____ .

6. The common name for the group

$$CH_3-CH_2-CH-$$
$$\overset{|}{CH_3}$$

is _____ ; the functional class name for the ether

$$CH_3-CH_2-CH-O-CH-CH_2-CH_3$$
$$\qquad\quad\overset{|}{CH_3}\qquad\overset{|}{CH_3}$$

is _____ .

7. The name s-butyl ether is adequate and a prefix di (for di-s-butyl ether) is unnecessary because _____
_____ .

8. The common name for the group

$$\qquad\qquad\overset{CH_3}{\overset{|}{}}$$
$$CH_3-CH_2-C-$$
$$\qquad\qquad\overset{|}{CH_3}$$

is _____ , that for the group

$$\triangleright$$

is _____ , and that for the ether

$$\qquad\qquad\overset{CH_3}{\overset{|}{}}$$
$$\triangleright-O-C-CH_2-CH_3$$
$$\qquad\qquad\overset{|}{CH_3}$$

is _____ .

SUBSTITUTIVE NAMES

In substitutive names of compounds containing an ether group, the ether functional group does not properly serve as the basis of the name. The RO group is regarded as a substituent and is named by adding oxy to the stem portion of the name of an alkyl group containing fewer than 5 carbons or to the full name of more complex alkyl groups. For example, the substituent CH_3-O- is named methoxy, and

$$CH_3-CH_2-\underset{\underset{\displaystyle CH_3}{|}}{CH}-CH_2-CH_2-O-$$

is named 3-methylpentyloxy. No particular preference is given to an alkoxy substituent in assigning position numbers.

9. Methyl isopropyl ether can be represented by the formula

_____.

A substitutive name for this ether will indicate an alkoxy substituent on a parent chain. The parent alkane chain will be called _____; the substituent, which appears on position number ____, will be called _____; and the complete substitutive name will be

_____.

10. The longest continuous chain of carbons in the formula

$$CH_3-CH_2-\underset{\underset{\displaystyle CH_3-CH_2-O}{|}}{CH}-CH_2-\underset{\underset{\displaystyle CH_3-CH-CH_3}{|}}{CH}-CH_3$$

contains ____(number) carbons. The name for this chain is _____. Substituents appear on carbons numbered _____. Two of the substituents are called methyl, and the third is called _____. A complete substitutive name for this ether is

_____.

11. A structural formula for 1,4-dimethoxy-2-pentene is

_____.

12. If stereochemistry were to be indicated, and the name of the compound were 1,4-diiso-butoxy-trans-2-pentene, the structural formula would be

_____.

13. The substitutive name for $Cl-CH_2-O-CH_3$ is _____.
The group $Cl-CH_2-$ may be named a chloromethyl group; the functional class name of this ether then becomes _____. This ether is sometimes erroneously called chloromethyl ether, a name which indicates _____ bound to oxygen.

45

14. The structural formula for chloromethyl ether will be _____.

15. A substitutive name for the alcohol

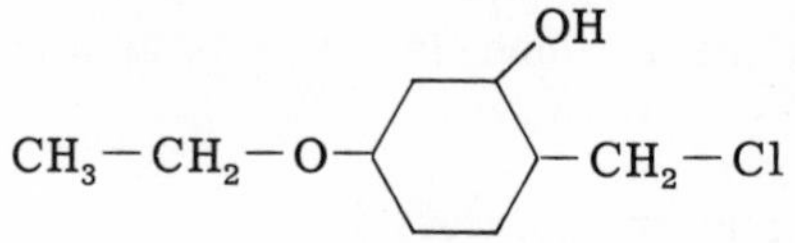

$$CH_3-CH_2-O-\overset{\displaystyle OH}{\bigcirc}-CH_2-Cl$$

will use_____ as the basis of the name and will specify two substituents, named _____ and _____. Correct numbering will assign the OH group to position number___ and the ethoxy substituent to position number ____. The complete substitutive name for this alcohol is

_____.

16. A substitutive name for the alkyne

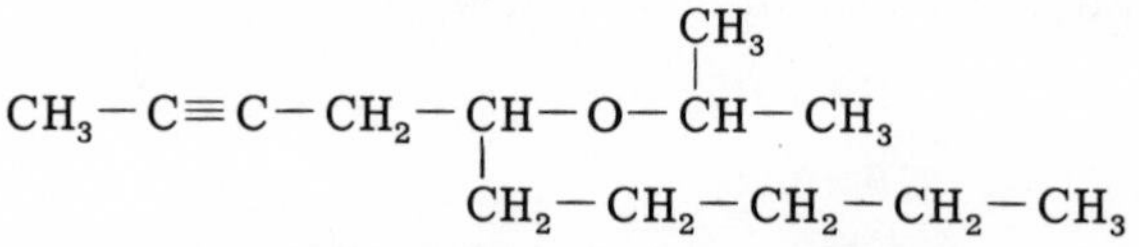

$$CH_3-C\equiv C-CH_2-\underset{\displaystyle CH_2-CH_2-CH_2-CH_2-CH_3}{CH}-O-\overset{\displaystyle CH_3}{CH}-CH_3$$

will be based on the longest continuous chain of carbons, containing_____(number) carbons. The alkyne name for this chain is_____. The functional group which is the basis of the name is assigned position number____ and the substituent, named _____, is on position number____. The complete substitutive name for this compound is

_____.

7
Carboxylic
Acids

Carboxylic acids are represented by the general formula

$$R-\overset{\overset{\displaystyle O}{\|}}{C}-OH$$

or, more conveniently for typing, $R-COOH$ or $R-CO_2H$. Names of carboxylic acids illustrate particularly well the problem of established usage in nomenclature. An International Congress held in Geneva, Switzerland, in 1892, attempted to establish rigid rules for nomenclature which would systematize names for all classes of compounds. No system of nomenclature has achieved unique usage, however. That is the reason we accept both methyl alcohol and methanol for CH_3OH. In nomenclature as in other situations involving persons, convenience and familiarity and usage may offset whatever rules are devised.

The common names of several acids were too firmly established to succumb to the hope of the Geneva Congress that all names not allowed by its rules would be discarded. The Geneva rules became the foundation on which the broader, current IUPAC rules are built, however, and many Geneva names survive in the IUPAC system. The substitutive IUPAC names we have studied so far are essentially Geneva names. The IUPAC system now not only accepts both common and Geneva names for carboxylic acids, but indicates preference for the common names of those acids containing fewer than six carbons.

To summarize, carboxylic acids containing fewer than six carbons are named preferably by common names; more complex structures are named by Geneva names, and a few acids are named by derived names. Carboxylic acids are the first class of compounds you have studied for which all IUPAC names are two-word names.

COMMON NAMES

The common names of acids are formed by adding to the proper stem the ending <u>ic</u> (occasionally, <u>oic</u>) and the separate word <u>acid</u>. The stems used for carboxylic acids are quite different from those learned for common names of alkyl groups. They are usually Latin or Greek in origin and often reflect the natural sources from which the acids were first isolated. The stems are associated with particular numbers of carbons and structures just as the stems for alkyl groups are.

Common names for some carboxylic acids are listed below. For the acids illustrated, these common names are the preferred IUPAC names. The stems, which will figure in names of acid derivatives, are underlined.

<u>form</u>ic acid	$H-COOH$
<u>acet</u>ic acid	CH_3-COOH
<u>propion</u>ic acid	CH_3-CH_2-COOH
<u>butyr</u>ic acid	$CH_3-CH_2-CH_2-COOH$
<u>isobutyr</u>ic acid	$CH_3-CH-COOH$
	$\qquad\ \ \ \ \ |$
	$\qquad\ \ \ \ CH_3$
<u>valer</u>ic acid	$CH_3-CH_2-CH_2-CH_2-COOH$
<u>isovaler</u>ic acid	$CH_3-CH-CH_2-COOH$
	$\qquad\ \ \ \ \ |$
	$\qquad\ \ \ \ CH_3$

Only the stems of names signifying 3 and 4 carbons in carboxylic acids resemble the stems of names of alkyl groups.

1. The stem for three carbons in an alkyl group is _____, and that for three carbons in a carboxylic acid is _____. The stem for 4 carbons in an alkyl group is _____, and that for four carbons in a carboxylic acid is _____.

All other stems for the common names of carboxylic acids are completely different from the stems used for alkyl groups of corresponding carbon content.

2. The most common carboxylic acid contains two carbons and may be represented by the structural formula _____. The common name for this acid is _____.

3. The stem "acet" will always signify____(number) carbons in a carboxylic acid or acid derivative.

4. Since there is only one position available for a substituent in acetic acid, no position designation is necessary. The common name for the substituted acid represented by the formula $Cl-CH_2-COOH$ is _____, and the common name for the acid represented by the formula $Cl_3C-COOH$ is _____.

Note that chloroacetic and trichloroacetic are single words. Acetic acid is the name of an individual compound, and modifiers (names of substituents) must be written as part of the same word.

5. t-Butoxy is the name of the substituent represented by the formula

_____,

and t-butoxyacetic acid may be represented by the formula

_____ .

Common names of carboxylic acids utilize either numbers or Greek letters to indicate the location of substituents with respect to the carboxyl group (COOH). Alpha (α) corresponds to the position adjacent to the carboxyl group (position 2); beta (β) corresponds to the position numbered 3; gamma (γ) corresponds to the position numbered 4; and so on. The Greek letter omega (ω) is often used to indicate a substituent on the terminal carbon away from the carboxyl group, regardless of the number of carbons intervening.

6. A structural formula representing α-chloropropionic acid may be drawn

_____ , and β-chloropropionic acid will be represented by the formula

_____ .

7. When the OH group is treated as a substituent, it is called a _____ group. The preferred IUPAC name (common name) for $CH_3-CH_2-CH_2-CH_2-COOH$ is _____ , and the substituted acid

$$CH_3-\underset{\underset{OH}{|}}{CH}-CH_2-CH_2-COOH$$

will be named _____ .

8. Valeric acid contains ____(number) carbons per molecule. Location of a substituent on the terminal carbon may be indicated by the Greek letter _____ .
A common name for $Br-CH_2-CH_2-CH_2-CH_2-COOH$ is _____ .

GENEVA NAMES

The systematic ending, oic, replaces the final e in the name of the alkane of corresponding carbon structure and is followed by "acid" as a separate word. For example, the one-carbon alkane is methane and the one-carbon carboxylic acid is methanoic acid (but the preferred IUPAC name is formic acid).

9. The Geneva name for CH_3-COOH is _____ and that for $CH_3-CH_2-CH_2-CH_2-COOH$ is _____ .

49

10. A structural formula for butanoic acid is _____.

The $-COOH$ group (carboxyl group) necessarily appears at the end of a chain of carbons and determines the numbering of chains in compounds named as alkanoic acids. The carbon in the $-COOH$ group is assigned position number 1, but no number is needed or used in the name to indicate its location. Substituents on the parent chain (the longest chain of which the $-COOH$ group is a part) are indicated in the Geneva name in exactly the same way as they would be in the name of the corresponding alkane.

11. A Geneva name for

$$CH_3$$
$$|$$
$$CH_2-CH_2-CH-CH_2-COOH$$
$$|$$
$$CH_3$$

will be based on a chain of____(number) carbons, for which the stem _____will be used. The name for the parent chain, including functional group, is _____; the substituent appears on position number____, and the complete Geneva name for the acid is

_____.

12. The parent chain in the formula

$$CH_3-CH_2$$
$$|$$
$$CH_3-CH_2-CH-CH_2-C-CH_2-COOH$$
$$|\qquad\qquad|$$
$$CH_3\qquad\;\;Cl$$

contains____(number) carbons. Substituents appear on carbons numbered _____.
The Geneva name for this acid is _____.

13. Substituents named ethynyl and ethoxy are represented by the formulas _____ and _____, respectively. A structural formula for 2-ethynyl-5-ethoxypentanoic acid may be written

_____.

Unsaturated carboxylic acids are named as alkenoic acids or alkynoic acids. The carboxyl group, serving as the basis of the Geneva name, takes precedence over other functional groups for numbering.

14. Because the carbon in the carboxyl group of an acyclic structure is always assigned position number ____, no number is necessary in the name to indicate its location.

The longest continuous chain containing both the carboxyl group and the alkene linkage will be the basis of the Geneva name of an alkenoic acid. The location of the alkene linkage will be indicated by a number preceding the stem in the Geneva name.

15. The Geneva name for $CH_3-CH=CH-COOH$ is _____.

16. The unsaturated acid, 9-decenoic acid, may be represented by the structural formula
_____.

17. The Geneva name for $CH_3-C\equiv C-COOH$ is_____, and that for
$CH_3-C\equiv C-CH_2-CH_2-COOH$ is_____. Substituents along the chain of unsaturated carboxylic acids are treated in exactly the same way as they are in names of other compounds.

18. The Geneva name for $CH_3-CH=CH-CH_2-\underset{\underset{Cl}{|}}{CH}-COOH$ is

_____.

19. The Geneva name for

$$CH_3-C\equiv C-\underset{\underset{\underset{CH_3}{|}}{CH_3-CH}}{CH}-CH_2-\underset{\underset{\underset{CH_2-CH_3}{|}}{O}}{CH}-CH_2-\underset{\underset{Br}{|}}{CH}-COOH$$

is _____.

20. Because of the geometry of some unsaturated linkages, geometrical isomers are possible for_____(alkenoic or alkynoic) acids but not for _____(alkenoic or alkynoic) acids.

21. A structural formula for 2-ethyl-<u>trans</u>-3-pentenoic acid may be drawn

_____.

The <u>cis</u> isomer of this acid would be represented by the structural formula

_____.

DERIVED NAMES

A few carboxylic acids are named as derivatives of <u>acetic acid</u>. (<u>Note</u>: acetic acid, <u>not</u> formic acid, the first member of the series). It may be convenient to draw a rectangle, literally or mentally, around the carboxyl group and the adjacent carbon. Substituent alkyl groups then stand out clearly for naming. The name of the substituent is written as part of the single word which precedes acid in the name. Substituent names again become part of the word they modify.

22. A structural formula for trimethylacetic acid may be drawn

_____ .

The Geneva name for this acid is _____ .

23. The derived name for the acid

$$CH_3-CH-CH_3$$
$$\ \ \ \ \ \ \ \ \ \ \ |$$
$$CH_3-CH-CH-COOH$$
$$\ \ \ \ \ \ \ \ \ |$$
$$\ \ \ \ \ \ \ \ CH_3$$

is _____ ; a Geneva name for this acid is

_____ .

24. The neopentyl group may be represented by the formula

_____ ,

and neopentylacetic acid by the formula

_____ .

Carboxylic acids containing a carboxyl group attached directly to a cycloalkane ring are usually named as <u>cycloalkanecarboxylic acids</u>. With the exception of numbering, substituted cycloalkanes are named exactly as they would be if the carboxylic group were absent; that name is then attached to <u>carboxylic acid</u> to complete the name of the acid. As the basis of the name, the carboxyl group takes precedence over other substituents on the ring so far as numbering is concerned: the carbon to which the carboxyl group is attached is assigned the lowest possible number, namely 1 for simple ring systems. No number designation for the carboxyl group is included in such a name.

25. Cyclopropanecarboxylic acid may be represented by the formula _____.

26. The formula

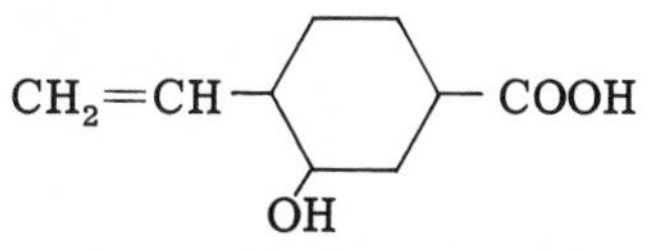

$$CH_2{=}CH{-}\bigcirc{-}COOH$$
$$OH$$

shows on the ring, besides the carboxyl group, two substituents which are named _____ and _____. Proper numbering assigns these substituents to positions numbered ___ and ___, respectively. A complete name for the acid is

_____.

27. In the formula

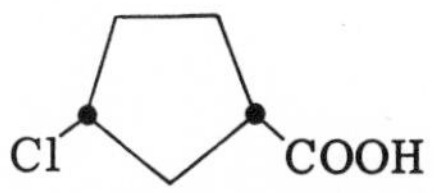

$$Cl{-}\bigcirc{-}COOH$$

which conveys information of geometrical significance, the substituents on the ring are _____(cis or trans) to each other and appear on positions numbered ___ and ___. A complete name for the acid, including specification of geometry, is

_____.

8
Acid Derivatives

ACID HALIDES AND ANHYDRIDES

If the OH portion of a carboxyl group is replaced by a halogen atom, the resulting structure is called an <u>acyl halide</u> or an <u>acid halide</u>. The group

$$R-\overset{\overset{\displaystyle O}{\|}}{C}-\qquad or \qquad R-CO-$$

is called an acyl group. Acyl halides, like carboxylic acids themselves, have two-word names which are formulated easily if the name of the corresponding acid is known. The "ic" ending of the acid name is replaced with "yl" ("oyl" for common names indicating more than 5 carbons), and the final word, acid, is replaced with the separate word chloride, bromide, or other halide, as required. That is, the <u>stem</u> of the acid name is followed by <u>yl</u> and the separate word <u>halide</u>. This form applies regardless of the system of nomenclature being used.

1. The common name for CH_3-COOH is _____; the stem of this acid name is _____; and the common name for $CH_3-CO-Cl$ is _____.

2. The Geneva name for $CH_3-CH_2-CH_2-CH_2-CH_2-COOH$ is _____, and the Geneva name for $CH_3-CH_2-CH_2-CH_2-CH_2-CO-Cl$ is _____.

3. α-Bromopropionic acid may be represented by the formula

_____,

and α-bromopropionyl bromide by the formula

_____.

A Geneva name for this acyl halide is _____.

4. Dicyclopropylacetyl chloride may be represented by the formula

_____ .

5. Octadecanoic acid, which contains _____ (number) carbon atoms, is commonly called stearic acid. The common name for $CH_3-(CH_2)_{16}-CO-Cl$ is _____ .

Acid anhydrides are easily named if one knows how to name the corresponding carboxylic acid: The final word, acid, is simply replaced by the word anhydride, regardless of which style of nomenclature is being used.

6. The common name for CH_3-COOH is _____ , and the common name of $CH_3-CO-O-CO-CH_3$ is _____ .

7. A structural formula for trimethylacetic acid is

_____ ,

and a structural formula for trimethylacetic anhydride is

_____ .

Acetic anhydride and trimethylacetic anhydride are simple anhydrides, that is, the two acyl groups are alike. Mixed anhydrides are also known; the two acyl groups in mixed anhydrides are not alike. Three-word names are used for mixed anhydrides, each acid being named separately (usually in order of increasing complexity) and the separate word anhydride completing the name.

8. A common name for $H-CO-O-CO-CH_2-CH_3$, which is an anhydride related to the two acids _____ and _____ , is

_____ .

9. A common name for the mixed anhydride

$$CH_3-\underset{\underset{\displaystyle CH_3}{|}}{CH}-CH_2-CO-O-CO-CH_3$$

is _____ .

10. 4-Methylhexanoic 2-ethylheptanoic anhydride may be represented by the formula

_____ .

ESTERS

Esters are compounds having an alkyl group and an acyl group attached to an oxygen atom:

$$\text{acyl group} \longrightarrow \boxed{R - \overset{\overset{\textstyle O}{\|}}{C}} - O - \boxed{R'} \longrightarrow \text{alkyl group}$$

For convenience in typing and writing, an ester may be represented by the general formula $R-COOR'$ or, turning the molecule around, $R'O-CO-R$ or $R'OOC-R$. Note that the alkyl group (R' in the illustrations here) is always clearly attached to an O.

Esters are named in the same manner as salts (even though esters and salts are completely different from each other in properties): two-word names are used. The alkyl group is named as one word, and the final word of the name is formed by adding the ending "ate" to the stem of the acid name. That is, "ic acid" is replaced by "ate." For example, acetic acid (ethanoic acid) will form an ester which will be called an acetate (ethanoate).

11. Methanoic acid is more often called by its common name, _____.
The second word of the Geneva name of an ester related to this acid will be
_____, and the second word of a common name for the ester will be

_____ .

12. Propionic acid is the common name for the acid whose Geneva name is
_____. The second word of the common name of an ester related to
this acid will be _____, and of a Geneva name, _____.

13. An ester formed from butyric acid will be called a _____ .

14. The ester whose formula may be written

$$CH_3 - CH_2 - CH_2 - \overset{\overset{\textstyle \|}{\textstyle O}}{\underset{}{C}} - O - CH_3$$

may be named _____ (common name).

15. The formula

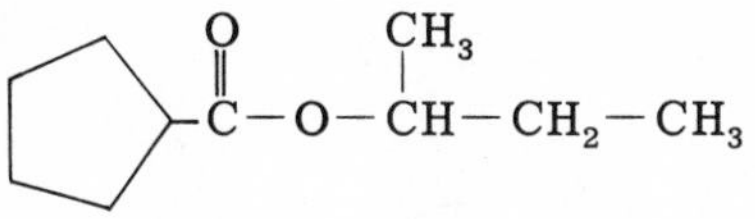

$$\text{cyclopentyl}-\overset{\displaystyle O}{\overset{\|}{C}}-O-\overset{\displaystyle CH_3}{\overset{|}{CH}}-CH_2-CH_3$$

shows attached to oxygen an alkyl group which is named _____. The name of the alkyl group is the first word in the name of the ester. The acid to which the ester is related is named _____, and the second word in the name of the ester becomes_____. The complete two-word name for the ester is _____.

16. A structural formula for trifluoroacetic acid is _____; a structural formula for the alkyl group isobutyl is

_____,

and a structural formula for isobutyl trifluoroacetate is

_____.

17. Isobutyric acid may be represented by the formula

_____,

and isobutyl isobutyrate by the formula

_____.

18. A common name for $CH_2{=}CH{-}CH_2{-}O{-}\overset{\displaystyle O}{\overset{\|}{C}}{-}H$ is _____.

19. Allyl propionate may be represented by the structural formula

_____, and vinyl acetate by the formula

_____.

57

20. A complex ester such as

$$CH_3-CH=C-CH_2-CH-CH_2-COO-CH_2-CH-CH_2-CH-CH_3$$
$$\qquad\qquad | \qquad\quad | \qquad\qquad\qquad\qquad\quad | \qquad\qquad |$$
$$\qquad\qquad Cl \qquad\quad CH_3 \qquad\qquad\qquad\qquad O-CH_3 \quad CH_3$$

may be named by an IUPAC name if we consider the alkyl group and the acyl group separately. The basis of the alkyl group name will be a chain of ____ (number) carbons with substituents on positions numbered ____ and ____. The substituents are named _____ and _____, respectively, and the name of the entire alkyl group is _____ _____. The acyl group contains a parent chain of ____ (number) carbons with a chloro substituent on position number ____ and a methyl substituent on position number ____. The complete name of the carboxylic acid to which the ester is related is _____, and the last word of the ester name will be _____. The complete IUPAC name of the ester will be _____ _____.

21. The ester

is conveniently named by combining a substitutive name for the alkyl group with <u>acetate</u>. The alkyl group will be named _____ and the ester will be named _____.

22. A structural formula representing <u>trans</u>-2-pentenyl acetate is

_____.

23. The compound represented by the formula

may be named _____.

24. Stearic acid is the common name for the acid containing ____ (number) carbons. Stearic acid may be represented by the formula _____, and methyl stearate by the formula

_____.

Aldehydes
and
Ketones

The group $-\overset{\overset{\displaystyle O}{\|}}{C}-$ is called a carbonyl group. The carbonyl group present in carboxylic acids and in acid derivatives is attached to oxygen (acids and esters), to halogen (acyl halides), and to nitrogen (amides), as well as to a hydrogen or an alkyl group. When the carbonyl group is attached only to hydrogens or carbons (alkyl groups), and not to any other atoms, the compounds are called aldehydes or ketones.

In aldehydes, at least one hydrogen is attached to the carbonyl group; in ketones, two hydrocarbon groups are attached to the carbonyl group.

1. The type of compound represented by the formula $CH_3-CH_2-\overset{\overset{\displaystyle}{C}}{\underset{\underset{\displaystyle O}{\|}}{}}-CH_3$ is _____.

2. The type of compound represented by the formula $CH_3-\overset{\overset{\displaystyle O}{\|}}{C}-H$ is _____.

3. The formula

$$H-\overset{\overset{\displaystyle}{C}}{\underset{\underset{\displaystyle O}{\|}}{}}-H$$

represents _____ (type of compound) and

represents _____ (type of compound).

For convenience in typing and writing, aldehydes are often represented by a condensed structural formula such as R$-$CHO. Note that the functional group is written $-$CHO rather than $-COH$ to avoid any confusion with alcohols. Ketones may be represented conveniently by a formula such as $R-CO-R$.

Nomenclature of aldehydes is closely related to that of carboxylic acids. The introductory section of Chapter 7 briefly describes the background of two types of names of carboxylic acids currently used in the IUPAC system. Both Geneva and common names of aldehydes are also used; both are one-word names.

Geneva names of aldehydes and ketones are one-word names formed by replacing the final e in the name of the hydrocarbon of corresponding carbon content and structure with the appropriate ending. The systematic ending for aldehyde is al; that for ketone is one (pronounced as in bone).

4. The formula $CH_3-CH_2-CH_2-CH_2-CHO$ represents an aldehyde containing five carbons. The Geneva name of the corresponding hydrocarbon is _____, and the Geneva name for the aldehyde is _____.

5. The formula $CH_3-CO-CH_3$ represents a ketone which may be named_____.

6. Cyclohexanone may be represented by the formula _____.

7. Propanal may be represented by the formula _____.

Since the aldehyde functional group must necessarily be at the end of the chain, it will always be position number 1 in parent chains named as aldehydes. No number designation for the aldehyde functional group is necessary in the name. The carbonyl group in some ketones, on the other hand, may appear at isomeric positions, and if so, a number designation is required in the name. When the carbonyl-containing compound is named as an alkanone the ketone functional group is given the lower possible number in the parent chain containing it. Substituent positions in both aldehydes and ketones are given the lower possible numbers after the proper number has been assigned to the carbonyl group.

8. There are two isomers which may be called pentanone; structural formulas for these isomers may be written _____ and
_____. The complete Geneva names for these isomers are _____ and _____, respectively.

9. A structural formula for 3-chloro-2-pentanone may be drawn

_____.

3-Chloropentanal may be represented by the formula

_____.

10. The hydrocarbon corresponding to the aldehyde

$$CH_3 - \underset{\underset{CH_3}{|}}{CH} - CH_2 - CH = CH - CHO$$

will have the substitutive name_____, and the Geneva name for the aldehyde itself will be_____.

11. The hydrocarbon corresponding to the aldehyde

$$CH_3 - \underset{\underset{CH_3}{|}}{C} = CH - CH_2 - CH_2 - CH_2 - CHO$$

will actually have the substitutive name_____. When the aldehyde itself is to be named as an aldehyde however, the $-CHO$ functional group takes precedence over any other functional groups for numbering. The carbonyl group becomes position number ____, the alkene linkage is assigned position number ____, and the methyl substituent appears on position number ____. The substitutive (Geneva) name for the aldehyde is

_____.

12. 8-Isopropoxy-6-vinyl-3-nonanone may be represented by the formula

_____.

When the $-CHO$ group is attached to a cycloalkyl group, the compound is named by adding "carboxaldehyde" to the name of the cycloalkane. (Recent IUPAC rules specify "carbaldehyde," but Chemical Abstracts uses "carboxaldehyde.") The position to which the $-CHO$ group is attached is designated position number 1.

13. The IUPAC name for [cyclopentane]$-CHO$ is _____.

14. The IUPAC name for CH_3-[cyclobutane]$-CHO$ is _____.

15. If one wished to represent cis-3-methylcyclobutanecarboxaldehyde by a structural formula which conveys geometrical information, the formula could be drawn as:

_____.

Some aldehydes and ketones contain other functional groups which may be used as the basis of the name of the compound. For example, a compound may contain both a ketone functional group and a carboxylic acid functional group. If another functional group is used as the basis of the name, the oxygen of the aldehyde or ketone carbonyl group is regarded as a substituent. It is designated oxo, and location is indicated by a number in the usual manner. When the oxygen of the carbonyl group is designated oxo, it receives no more preference for numbering than any other substituent.

16. 3-Oxobutanoic acid may be represented by the structural formula _____.

17. The structural formula for 6-oxohexanoic acid may be drawn

_____.

In addition to being a carboxylic acid, this compound may also be classified as

_____.

18. "Queen substance," a bee sex attractant isolated from queen honey bee glands, is 9-oxo-trans-2-decenoic acid, which may be represented by the structural formula

_____.

19. An IUPAC name for the ester

$$CH_2{=}CH{-}O{-}\overset{\overset{\displaystyle O}{\|}}{C}{-}CH_2{-}\underset{\underset{\displaystyle CH_3}{|}}{CH}{-}CH_2{-}CO{-}\underset{\underset{\displaystyle CH_3}{|}}{CH}{-}CH_3$$

will specify the alkyl group bound to oxygen, namely, _____, and will treat the oxygen of the ketone carbonyl in the acyl group as a substituent designated _____. The name of the acid related to this ester is _____,
and the complete name for the ester is _____.

20. The compound represented by the formula

may be named as an aldehyde; the basis of the name, without specifying numbering or substituent, will be _____, and proper numbering of the ring will assign position number____ to the alkene linkage. The complete name for the substituted aldehyde will be _____.

62

ALDEHYDES: COMMON AND DERIVED NAMES

Common names of aldehydes (R—CHO) are based on those of the corresponding carboxylic acids (R—COOH). The common names of carboxylic acids were originally chosen to reflect the origin of the compound and may have little resemblance to the stems associated with alkyl groups of the same carbon skeleton. Several common acids are illustrated and named below; the stem of the name is underlined in each name. Aldehydes having the same carbon skeleton, with the —CHO group replacing the —COOH group, may be named by adding aldehyde to the stem of the acid name.

Common Names of Some Carboxylic Acids

formic acid   H—COOH

acetic acid CH_3—COOH

propionic acid CH_3—CH_2—COOH

butyric acid CH_3—CH_2—CH_2—COOH

isobutyric acid CH_3—$\overset{\overset{\displaystyle CH_3}{|}}{CH}$—COOH

valeric acid CH_3—CH_2—CH_2—CH_2—COOH

isovaleric acid CH_3—$\overset{\overset{\displaystyle CH_3}{|}}{CH}$—$CH_2$—COOH

21. The common name for H—CHO is formaldehyde, and the common name for CH_3—CHO is _____.

22. The common name for CH_3—CH_2—CHO is _____, and that for

$$CH_3-\underset{\underset{\displaystyle CH_3}{|}}{CH}-CH_2-CHO$$

is _____.

23. A condensed structural formula for isobutyraldehyde may be drawn _____.

24. Only for aldehydes containing three and four carbons do the stems of the common names resemble the stems of alkyl groups of the same carbon content. The relationship among frequently used common name stems, carbon content, and IUPAC stems is illustrated by the following table.

Common Name Stem	Total Number of Carbons	Geneva Name Stem	Geneva Name of R—CHO
form	_____	_____	_____
acet	_____	_____	_____
valer	_____	_____	_____

In common names, Greek letters (α, β, γ, etc.) or numerals designate the positions of substituents. For aldehydes, alpha (α) or 2 refers to the carbon to which the —CHO group is attached.

25. The substituted aldehyde, α-chloropropionaldehyde, may be represented by the structural formula

_____ .

26. The compound represented by the formula

$$CH_3-CH-CH_2-CHO$$
$$\quad\quad | $$
$$\quad\quad OH$$

may be named as a substituted aldehyde by the common name _____
and by the Geneva name _____ .

27. In the unsaturated aldehyde $CH_3-CH_2-CH=CH-CH_2-CHO$, the alkene linkage appears between the _____ (Greek letters) carbons.

28. γ-Bromovaleraldehyde may be represented by the formula

_____ .

Derived names are used for a few aldehydes. The basis for the derived name is acetaldehyde (note: not formaldehyde). It is helpful to sketch, literally or mentally, a rectangle around the $-CHO$ group and the α-carbon. The substituents stand out clearly and are named as they are in common names, in alphabetical order or in order of increasing complexity. Because acetaldehyde is the name of an individual compound, derived names of aldehydes are single-word names. Derived names are useful particularly for lists of compounds in which one wishes to emphasize changing substituent groups.

29. Trimethylacetaldehyde may be represented by the structural formula

_____ .

30. A derived name for
$$\quad\quad\quad\quad\quad CH_3-CH-CH_3$$
$$\quad\quad\quad\quad\quad\quad\quad\quad | $$
$$CH_3-CH-CH-CHO \text{ is } \underline{\hspace{6cm}} .$$
$$\quad\quad\quad | $$
$$\quad\quad\quad CH_3$$

31. A condensed structural formula for dimethylneopentylacetaldehyde may be drawn

_____.

The Geneva name for this aldehyde is _____.

KETONES: COMMON NAMES

Common names of ketones are multiple-word names ending in <u>ketone</u>. The alkyl groups attached to the carbonyl group are specified by common names just as they are for names of ethers. If both alkyl groups are alike (that is, if the ketone is symmetrical), <u>dialkyl</u> is used. Like <u>ether</u>, <u>ketone</u> requires two alkyl groups. Nonetheless, practice favors, for example, <u>ethyl ether</u> but <u>diethyl ketone</u>. That's just the way the custom capers.

32. The common name for $CH_3-CH_2-CO-CH_2-CH_3$ is _____.

33. The structural formula for 4-methyl-2-pentanone is

_____.

The common name for this ketone is _____.

34. A common name for ▷—CO—◁ is _____.

35. Ethyl allyl ketone may be represented by the structural formula
_____. Relative to the carbonyl group, the alkene linkage in this ketone appears between _____ (Greek letters) carbons. The Geneva name for this unsaturated ketone will assign position number ____ to the carbonyl group and position number ____ to the alkene linkage; the complete Geneva name will be _____.

36. Methyl vinyl ketone may be represented by the formula _____. Relative to the carbonyl group, the alkene linkage appears between _____ (Greek letters) carbons.

A few symmetrical ketones are named in a fashion that reflects a relationship to carboxylic acids from which the ketones may be prepared. Acetone, $CH_3-CO-CH_3$, is the primary example of this system of nomenclature and the only one whose continued use is not discouraged by the IUPAC. The alkyl groups are identical with that in the carboxylic acid whose common name stem is combined with <u>one</u> to form the name of the symmetrical ketone.

10
Amines
and
Ammonium Compounds

Amines are organic compounds related to ammonia, both in structure and chemical behavior. The trivalent nitrogen atom in amines is bound only to alkyl groups and hydrogens. If only one hydrogen of ammonia is replaced by an alkyl group (for example, CH_3-NH_2), the amine is classified as a primary amine; if two alkyl groups are bound to the nitrogen, the amine is classified as a secondary amine; and if three alkyl groups are bound to nitrogen (no hydrogens bound to nitrogen), the amine is a tertiary amine.

1. The compound represented by the formula $CH_3-CH_2-NH-CH_2-CH_3$ is classified as a _____ amine.

2. The compound represented by the formula

$$CH_3 - \overset{\overset{\displaystyle CH_3}{|}}{N} - CH_3$$

is classified as a _____ amine.

3. When alkyl groups are represented by the general symbol, R, primary amines may be represented by the generalized formula _____, secondary amines by the generalized formula _____, and tertiary amines by the generalized formula

_____.

Note that the classification of amines depends on the degree of substitution on the nitrogen atom, not on the nature of the alkyl group or groups. The classification of alcohols, for example, depends on the nature of the alkyl group, not on the oxygen, since only one alkyl group can be attached to oxygen in an alcohol.

4. The alcohol represented by the formula

$$CH_3-\underset{\underset{CH_3}{|}}{\overset{\overset{CH_3}{|}}{C}}-OH$$

is classified as a _____ alcohol, and the amine represented by the formula

$$CH_3-\underset{\underset{CH_3}{|}}{\overset{\overset{CH_3}{|}}{C}}-NH_2$$

is classified as a _____ amine.

5. The alcohol represented by the formula

$$CH_3-CH_2-\underset{\underset{OH}{|}}{CH}-CH_3$$

is classified as a _____ alcohol, and the amine represented by the formula

$$CH_3-CH_2-\underset{\underset{NH_2}{|}}{CH}-CH_3$$

is classified as a _____ amine.

6. The alcohol represented by the formula

$$CH_3-\underset{\underset{CH_3}{|}}{CH}-CH_2-OH$$

is classified as a _____ alcohol, and the amine represented by the formula

$$CH_3-\underset{\underset{CH_3}{|}}{CH}-CH_2-NH_2$$

is classified as a _____ amine.

Amines having the general formula $R-NH_2$ are named by combining the ending "amine" with the name of the alkyl group, R. It is permissible to combine the ending "amine" with the name of the corresponding hydrocarbon, $R-H$, but this type of nomenclature is preferably restricted to complex cyclic compounds. Secondary and tertiary amines in which all alkyl groups are alike are named by incorporating the appropriate multiplying prefix ("di" or "tri") before the alkyl group name. Although the ending "amine" is preferably combined with the name of an alkyl group rather than with that of a hydrocarbon, "amine" is an ending like "ol" and "ene," and names of amines are one-word names. "Amine" may be regarded as a kind of contraction of "ammonia," the name of an individual compound.

7. The amine represented by the formula CH_3-NH_2 is called _____, and that represented by the formula $CH_3-CH_2-NH_2$ is called _____.

8. Trimethylamine may be represented by the formula

_____.

9. $\underline{t}$-Butylamine may be represented by the formula

_____

and is classified as a _____ amine.

10. The formula $CH_3-CH_2-\underset{\underset{CH_3}{|}}{CH}-NH_2$ represents _____ (name).

11. The alkyl group attached to nitrogen in the formula

$$CH_3-\underset{\underset{CH_3-CH_2}{|}}{\overset{\overset{CH_3}{|}}{CH}}-CH_2-\underset{\underset{CH_3-CH_2}{|}}{\overset{\overset{CH_3}{|}}{C}}-CH_2-CH_2-NH_2$$

is named _____, and the name of the amine itself is _____.

12. 1-Ethylpentylamine may be represented by the formula

_____.

13. $\underline{trans}$-2-Isobutylcyclohexylamine may be represented by the formula

_____.

14. Tricyclopropylamine may be represented by the formula _____.

Unsymmetrical secondary and tertiary amines (all alkyl groups not alike) are named as N-substituted derivatives of a primary amine. The primary amine with the largest or most complex alkyl group is chosen as the parent amine for the name. For example, $CH_3-CH_2-NH-CH_3$ is named N-methylethylamine. Note that location of substituents on nitrogen is designated by an italicized capital N set off from the rest of the word just as is any other position designation.

15. The amine represented by the formula

$$CH_3-\underset{\underset{CH_3}{|}}{CH}-CH_2-NH-CH_2-CH=CH_2$$

may be named as a derivative of the primary amine _____. The secondary amine will be named _____.

16. The tertiary amine $CH_3-(CH_2)_9-N(CH_3)_2$ will be named

_____.

17. N,N-Dimethyl-4-vinylcyclohexylamine may be represented by the formula

_____.

When amine is the ending of the IUPAC name, the $-NH_2$ group (amino group) takes precedence over all other substituents or functional groups for numbering the parent chain.

18. An IUPAC name for

$$CH_3-\underset{\underset{CH_3}{|}}{CH}-CH_2-CH_2-\underset{\underset{NH_2}{|}}{CH}-CH_3$$

will indicate the amine functional group on carbon number ____, and methyl substituents on carbons numbered ____ and ____. A complete IUPAC name for the amine will be

_____.

19. For an IUPAC name ending in amine, proper numbering of the parent chain in the formula

$$CH_3-CH_2-\underset{\underset{CH_3-CH_2}{|}}{CH}-CH_2-CH=CH-CH_2-CH_2-CH_2-CH_2-CH_2-CH_2-NH_2$$

will designate the position of the alkene linkage by the number ____, and the position of the ethyl substituent by the number ____. The complete IUPAC name for this amine is

_____.

20. An IUPAC name for the amine represented by the formula

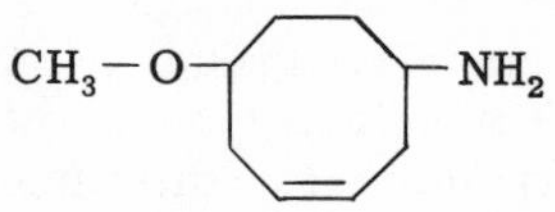

$$CH_3-O-\underset{\text{(ring)}}{\bigcirc}-NH_2$$

is _____.

21. The formula

$$CH_3-CH_2-\underset{\underset{CH_3}{|}}{CH}-CH=\underset{\underset{\underset{CH_3}{|}}{N-CH_2-CH_3}}{C}-CH_3$$

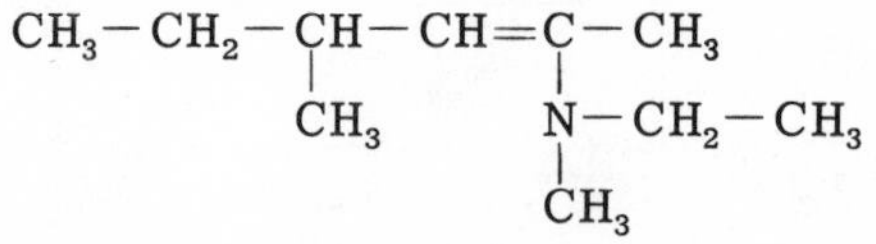

indicates a substituted amine. The parent compound (unsaturated primary amine without substituents) will be named _____. Three methyl substituents appear on positions numbered _____; an ethyl substituent appears on position ____. The complete IUPAC name for this substituted amine is

_____.

22. The compound represented by the formula

$$CH_3-CH_2-\underset{\underset{OH}{|}}{CH}-\underset{\underset{NH_2}{|}}{CH}-CH_2-CH_3$$

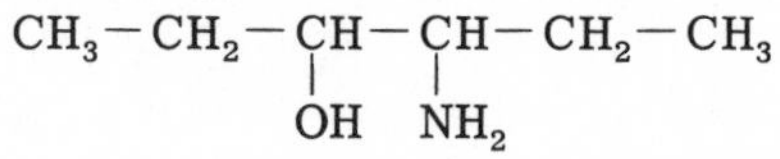

may be named as an amine or as an alcohol. When the compound is named as an amine, the substituent will be called _____, and the full IUPAC name will be

_____. When the compound is named as an alcohol, the substituent will be called amino, and the full IUPAC name will be

_____.

23. A formula which conveys geometrical as well as other structural information for trans-2-aminocyclopentanol may be drawn

_____.

24. cis-2-Hydroxycyclopentylamine may be represented by the formula

_____.

70

25. The compound represented by the formula

$$(CH_3)_2N-CH_2-\underset{\underset{\displaystyle CH_3}{|}}{CH}-CH_2-CO-CH_3$$

may be named as a ketone with a _____ substituent on position number ___ and a methyl substituent on position number ____. The complete substitutive name for this ketone is _____.

26. A structural formula for ethyl 2-diethylamino-3-ethoxydecanoate may be drawn

_____.

Compounds containing two or three amino groups may be named as alkanediamines and alkanetriamines. Numbers preceding the alkane portion of the name indicate location of the principal functional groups. Note that the alternate names given as answers in frames 19 and 20 follow this style.

27. Products produced by decaying flesh are $H_2N-CH_2-CH_2-CH_2-CH_2-NH_2$ and $H_2N-CH_2-CH_2-CH_2-CH_2-CH_2-NH_2$, commonly called putrescine and cadaverine, respectively. IUPAC names for these amines are _____ and _____, respectively.

28. 1,6-Hexanediamine, used in the manufacture of nylon, may be represented by the formula

_____.

29. 3-Methyl-2,4-pentanediamine may be represented by the formula

_____.

30. 1,2-Ethanediamine is more commonly called ethylenediamine. Ethylenediamine may be represented by the formula _____.

Other diamines of general formula $H_2N-(CH_2)_n-NH_2$ may be named as polymethylenediamines. (Recall polymethylene glycols, Chapter 3.)

31. 1,6-Hexanediamine, _____(formula), may also be named _____.

32. Tetramethylenediamine may be represented by the formula
_____ .

AMMONIUM COMPOUNDS

Like ammonia itself, amines are related directly to ammonium salts. Although these salts are sometimes named, for example, as alkylamine hydrochlorides, they are better named as ammonium salts. In whatever name is used for the amine itself, the ending amine is changed to ammonium and the anion is specified as a separate final word, for example, alkylammonium chloride for $R-\overset{+}{N}H_3\,Cl^-$.

33. The amine represented by the formula $(CH_3-CH_2)_2NH$ and commonly called _____ is directly related to the salt $(CH_3-CH_2)_2\overset{+}{N}H_2\,Cl^-$, which is named
_____ .

34. In the amine, nitrogen is_____ (multiplying prefix) -covalent, and in the salt it is _____(multiplying prefix) -covalent. Bonding between N and the anion in the salt is _____ .

35. N-Isopropyl-s-butylamine may be represented by the formula

_____ ,

and N-isopropyl-s-butylammonium perchlorate by the formula

_____ .

36. N-Allyl-N-isobutyl-1-ethylhexylammonium iodide may be represented by the formula

_____ .

37. Hydroxylamine, whose formula is_____ , is usually marketed as a salt, commonly called hydroxylamine hydrochloride. The salt can be represented by the formula _____ and may be named as an ammonium salt,
_____ .

Ammonium compounds in which four alkyl groups are bound to nitrogen are called quaternary ammonium compounds.

38. An example of a quaternary ammonium chloride is _____ .

39. Dodecyl is the name for an alkyl group containing _____ (number) carbons. $\underline{N},\underline{N},\underline{N}$-Trimethyldodecylammonium iodide may be represented by the formula
_____ and may be classified as a
_____ salt.

40. $\underline{N},\underline{N},\underline{N}$-Trimethyldodecylammonium hydroxide may be represented by the formula
_____ and may be classified
as a _____ hydroxide.

41. With R symbolizing an alkyl group, a quaternary ammonium hydroxide may be represented by the generalized formula _____.

42. In quaternary ammonium compounds, nitrogen is _____ (multiplying prefix) -covalent; bonding between nitrogen and the anion is _____.

11
Aromatic
Hydrocarbons

Benzene, the parent aromatic hydrocarbon, is symbolized in various ways:

$$C_6H_6,$$

The orientation of the hexagon does not matter.

Benzene serves as the basis of the names of many substituted benzenes. For an alkyl-substituted benzene such as

$$-R \text{ or } C_6H_5-R$$

the name of the alkyl group is followed by benzene to form a one-word name; since all positions in benzene are equivalent, no number is needed in the name to indicate position of a single substituent.

1. The aromatic hydrocarbon represented by the formula $C_6H_5-CH_2-CH_3$ or

$$-CH_2-CH_3$$

will be named _____.

2. The ethynyl group may be represented by the formula _____, and ethynylbenzene by the formula

_____.

3. s-Butylbenzene may be represented by the formula_____.

4. The alkyl group attached to C_6H_5- in the formula

$$C_6H_5-CH_2-\underset{\underset{CH_3}{|}}{\overset{\overset{CH_3}{|}}{C}}-CH_3$$

is called a_____ group, and the substituted benzene is named _____.

Sometimes a chemist may prefer to regard the benzene portion of the molecule as a substituent rather than as the basis of the name. Such an occasion may occur when a list of related compounds is being compiled. As a substituent, C_6H_5- or

is named phenyl and is treated as any other substituent. For convenience, phenyl is frequently symbolized ϕ or Ph.

5. Ethynylbenzene, represented by the formula

_____,

may be named as a substituted acetylene. The name then will be _____.

6. An IUPAC name for

$$CH_3-CH=CH-\underset{\underset{CH_3}{|}}{CH}-CH_2-\underset{\underset{CH_2-CH_2-CH_3}{|}}{CH}-\phi$$

with phenyl being treated as a substituent like methyl, will use as the basis of the name a hydrocarbon chain named_____. The methyl substituent appears on position number ____, and the phenyl substituent on position number____. The complete IUPAC name for the substituted alkene is _____.

7. A formula for 5-phenyldodecane may be drawn

_____.

8. Allylbenzene, represented by the formula

_____,
may be named as a substituted alkene: _____. The isomer, propenyl-
benzene

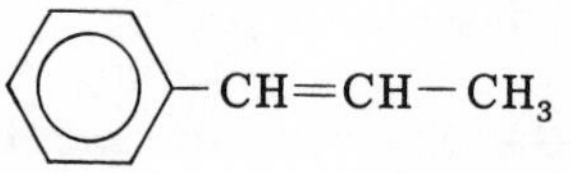

$\langle\!\!\langle\bigcirc\rangle\!\!\rangle$ — CH=CH — CH$_3$

may also be named as a substituted alkene: _____.

When two or more substituents are attached to the benzene ring, isomers are possible, and position designations must be used. Two different position designations are used: numbers and letters.

When numbers are used, one of the substituted positions will always be numbered 1, and the other positions in the ring are numbered 2 through 6, in the fashion that will assign the smallest possible numbers to the substituted positions.

9. In the formula

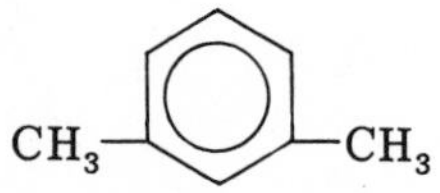

CH$_3$—$\langle\bigcirc\rangle$—CH$_3$

the methyl substituents appear on positions numbered ___ and ___.

10. 1,2-Diethylbenzene may be represented by the formula

_____.

11. The formula

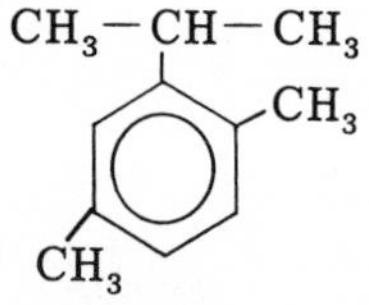

CH$_3$—CH—CH$_3$
$\langle\bigcirc\rangle$ CH$_3$
CH$_3$

pictures substituents on positions numbered ___, ___, and ___ (the lowest numbers which can be used). The name of the compound represented by this formula is

_____.

12. Mesitylene is a common name often used for 1,3,5-trimethylbenzene,

_____ (formula).

   For most disubstituted benzenes, chemists use letters more frequently than numbers to designate positions of substitution: o-(standing for and read ortho-) is used for compounds in which substituents appear on positions numbered 1 and 2; m-(for meta-) signifies substituents on positions 1 and 3; and p-(for para-) signifies substituents on positions numbered 1 and 4. These letter designations are prefixes which are italicized and set off from the rest of the names by hyphens.

13. Xylene is a common name for dimethylbenzene. There are three isomeric xylenes known:

   o-xylene, _____ ,(formula)

   m-xylene, _____ (formula),

   p-xylene, _____ (formula).

14. 1,4-Diisopropylbenzene may also be called _____ .

15. The two alkyl substituents in the formula

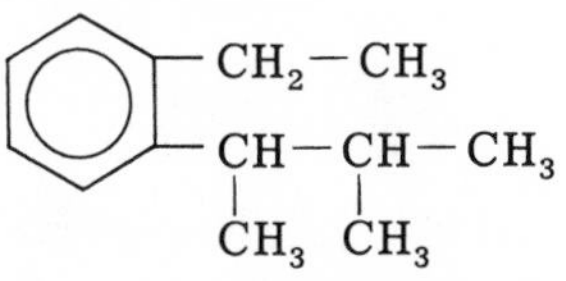

are _____ (o-, m-, or p-) to each other.

16. <u>m</u>–Ethylvinylbenzene can be represented by the formula

_____.

17. 1–Isobutyl-2-hexylbenzene may also be named _____.

Methylbenzene is most often called toluene, and <u>toluene</u> is actually used as the basis of names. That is, toluene is treated as a parent compound just as benzene is. When <u>toluene</u> is used in this way, the carbon to which the methyl group is attached is position number 1.

18. 3–Ethyltoluene may be represented by the formula_____.

19. <u>p-t</u>-Butyltoluene may be represented by the formula _____.

20.

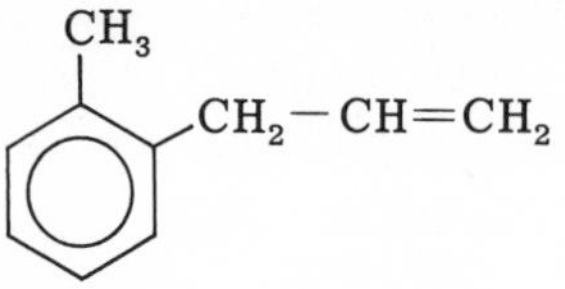

    CH_3
    $CH_2-CH=CH_2$
     may be named as a substituted toluene, _____.

21. Named as a substituted benzene

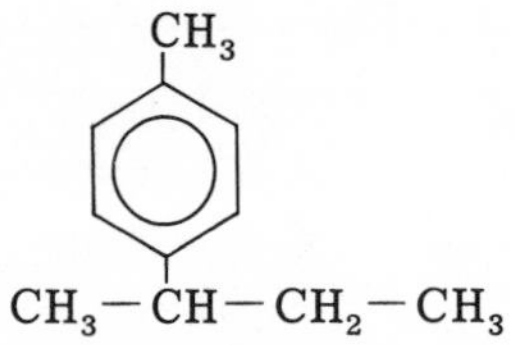

    CH_3

    $CH_3-CH-CH_2-CH_3$

will be called _____; named as a substituted toluene, the same compound will be called _____ .

Some other substituted benzenes are also treated as parent compounds like toluene.

22. For example, vinylbenzene, represented by the formula

_____,

is most often called styrene.

23. p-Isobutylstyrene may be represented by the formula

_____.

The two positions in the vinyl group of styrene are designated by the Greek letters, alpha and beta, as illustrated in the following formula:

$$\langle\bigcirc\rangle\text{—CH}=\text{CH}_2$$
$$\quad\quad\quad \alpha \quad \beta$$

24. α-Methylstyrene may be represented by the formula

_____; its isomer, β-methylstyrene may be represented by the formula

_____.

Another isomer, 3-methylstyrene, may be represented by the formula

_____.

25. Named as a substituted styrene,

$$\langle\bigcirc\rangle\begin{array}{l}\text{—C}=\text{CH}_2 \\ \ \ \ | \\ \text{CH}_2\text{—CH}_2\text{—CH}_3\end{array}$$

will be called _____; named as a substituted alkene, the same compound will be called _____. The choice of name often depends upon the context in which one wishes to use the name.

12

Substitution
Products
from
Aromatic Hydrocarbons

Just as with aliphatic hydrocarbons, hydrogens in aromatic hydrocarbons may be replaced by a variety of substituent groups. Substituted benzenes are named in essentially the same way as are substituted alkanes.

1. The substituted benzene represented by the formula

is named _____; that represented by the formula

is named _____; and that represented by the formula

is named _____.

The relative positions of substituents in multiply-substituted benzenes are indicated by letters (o-, m- or p- for disubstituted compounds) or by numbers. When numbers are used in the name of a substituted benzene, any substituent may be assigned position number 1 with the limitation that the smallest possible numbers designating positions of substituents must be used.

80

2. Formulas for three isomeric dichlorobenzenes may be drawn

_____ , _____ , and _____ ;
the compounds represented by these formulas may be named _____ ,
_____ and _____ (letters used to
designate relative positions of substitution), respectively, or _____ ,
_____ and _____ (numbers used to
designate positions of substitution), respectively.

3. m-Nitrochlorobenzene may be represented by the formula

_____ .
If numbers are used in the name, m-nitrochlorobenzene may be named
_____ or _____ .

4. Picryl chloride is a common name for the very reactive compound

The smallest numbers which can be used in a systematic name to indicate the positions of the
substituents in picryl chloride are ____ , ____ , ____ , and ____ . A systematic name for this substituted benzene, with numbers being used to indicate positions of substitution, is

_____ .

5. 2,4,6-Trinitrotoluene, commonly known as TNT, may be represented by the formula

_____ .

6. Even though the formulas for picryl chloride (frame 4) and TNT (frame 5) closely resemble each other, the positions to which the nitro substituents are attached are numbered
differently when the compounds are named as derivatives of hydrocarbons. Different numbers

are used because _____
_____
_____ .

   In compounds related to alkylbenzenes, a substituent may be bound to a carbon in the benzene nucleus or to a carbon in the alkyl group. The alkyl group is usually called a side chain.

   7. Three isomeric formulas may be drawn to represent compounds formed by replacing a hydrogen in the aromatic nucleus of toluene by a chlorine atom. The three formulas are

_____ , _____ , and _____ ,
and the three substituted toluenes may be named _____ ,
_____ , and _____ , respectively.

   8. A fourth isomer, in which the chloro substituent appears on the side chain rather than in the benzene nucleus, may be drawn:

_____ .

   When the substituent appears on the side chain of toluene, the position of substitution may be designated by the Greek letter <u>alpha</u> (α).

   9. The substituted toluene, —CH_2—Cl, may be named _____ .

   10. α-Nitrotoluene may be represented by the formula

_____ .

   For purposes of nomenclature, the group

—CH_2—

is most often regarded as an alkyl group and is named <u>benzyl</u>. The name benzyl is used in the same way as the name methyl.

11. A common name for the compound represented by the formula

$$\text{C}_6\text{H}_5-\text{CH}_2-\text{Cl}$$

is _____; a common name for the alcohol

$$\text{C}_6\text{H}_5-\text{CH}_2-\text{OH}$$

is _____, and a common name for the ether

$$\text{CH}_3-\text{O}-\text{CH}_2-\text{C}_6\text{H}_5$$

is _____.

12. The substituted benzyl chloride,

$$\text{O}_2\text{N}-\text{C}_6\text{H}_4-\text{CH}_2-\text{Cl}$$

may be named by the common name, _____.

13. o-Methoxybenzyl alcohol may be represented by the formula

_____.

Phenyl and benzyl are names that are sometimes confused by beginning students.

14. Phenylmagnesium bromide is a Grignard reagent represented by the formula

_____,

and benzylmagnesium bromide is represented by the formula

_____.

15. Allyl phenyl ether,

_____(formula),
and vinyl benzyl ether,

_____(formula),
are isomers.

16. Recall that styrene may serve as a parent name for substituted styrenes. Styrene is represented by the formula

_____.

17. There are five isomeric bromostyrenes for which formulas and names may be written as follows:

Formulas	Names (all bromostyrenes)
_____	_____
_____	_____
_____	_____
_____	_____
_____	_____

84

18. β-Nitrostyrene may be represented by the formula

_____.

19. 2,4-Difluorostyrene may be represented by the formula

_____.

20. If the compound represented by the formula

is named as a substituted styrene, the substituent in the 4-position will be named
_____, and the name of the compound will be _____.

When hydrogen in a hydrocarbon is replaced by the functional group $-SO_3H$ (or $-SO_2-OH$), the compound is called a sulfonic acid. Sulfonic acids are named by combining the name of the parent <u>hydrocarbon</u> (not alkyl group) with <u>sulfonic</u> to form one word followed by the separate word <u>acid</u>. For example, CH_3-SO_3H is named methanesulfonic acid. When it serves as the basis of a name, the functional group $-SO_3H$ takes precedence over all others in being assigned the lowest possible position number.

21. The compound $C_6H_5-SO_3H$ is named _____.

22. p-Bromobenzenesulfonic acid may be represented by the structural formula

_____.

23. 3,5-Dinitrobenzenesulfonic acid may be represented by the structural formula

_____.

85

24. When named as a derivative of toluene,

$$CH_3-\langle \bigcirc \rangle-SO_3H$$

will be named _____.

Note that the sulfonic acid functional group is assigned position number 1, even though toluene is considered the parent hydrocarbon.

Esters of sulfonic acids, $R-SO_2-O-R'$, are called sulfonates.

25. The ester represented by the formula

$$C_6H_5-SO_2-O-CH_2-CH_3$$

is named _____.

26. Cyclohexyl p-nitrobenzenesulfonate may be represented by the structural formula

_____.

27. The ester represented by the structural formula

$$O_2N-\langle \bigcirc \rangle-CH_2-O-SO_2-\langle \bigcirc \rangle-CH_3$$

may be named _____.

Bridged Ring Systems

Saturated hydrocarbon systems consisting of two rings which have two or more carbons in common are called bicycloalkanes. The stem which replaces "alk" in a specific name corresponds to the total number of carbons in the two rings.

1. The hydrocarbon represented by the formula

$$CH_2-CH-CH_2$$
$$CH_2 \quad CH_2$$
$$CH_2-CH-CH_2$$

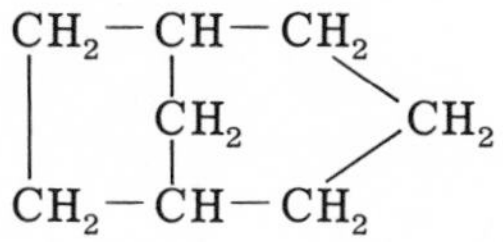

is a bicycloalkane containing a total of ____ (number) carbons in the two rings; it will be called a _____.

2. The hydrocarbon represented by the formula

$$CH_2-CH$$
$$CH_2$$
$$CH_2-CH$$

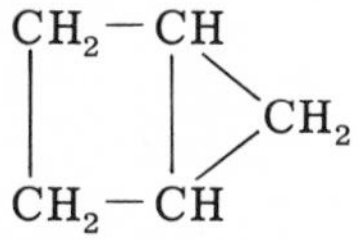

will be called a _____.

The two tertiary carbons in bicycloalkanes are called bridge-heads, and the bonds or chains of carbons connecting the bridge-heads are called bridges.

3. The two bridge-heads in the bicyclooctane formula of frame 1 are separated from each other by three bridges containing ____ , ____ , and ____ (numbers) carbons, respectively.

4. The two bridge-heads in the bicyclopentane formula of frame 2 are separated from each other by three bridges containing ____ , ____ , and ____ (numbers) carbons, respectively.

These numbers, designating the length of the bridges, are used in the full name of a bicycloalkane to differentiate it from isomeric bicycloalkanes. The style is illustrated by the name bicyclo[3.2.1]octane. Note that the numbers are arranged in descending order, are separated from each other by periods, and are enclosed in brackets. The name is a one-word name without any space separation between parts.

5. The full name for the bicyclopentane illustrated in frame 2 is

_____.

Bicycloalkanes, like cycloalkanes, are conveniently represented by geometric figures. The formulas:

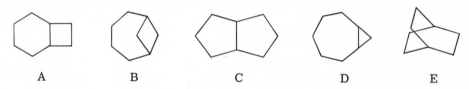

are equivalent representations of bicyclo[3.2.1]octane. The last figure is intended to show the actual geometry of the molecule.

Several isomeric bicyclooctanes may be represented by formulas, five of which are:

A   B   C   D   E

These isomeric bicyclooctanes are differentiated from each other by full names which include numbers.

6. The distinguishing, full name for:

formula A is _____;

formula B is _____;

formula C is _____;

formula D is _____;

formula E is _____.

Note that the numbers in brackets account for all carbons other than the bridgeheads in the bicycloalkane framework; the sum of these numbers always equals two less than the number of carbons signified by the stem in the name.

Numbering of a bicycloalkane to indicate location of substituents begins at one bridgehead, proceeds around the longest bridge to the other bridge-head, continues around the second longest bridge back to the number 1 position (original bridge-head), and is completed across the shortest bridge. The numbered formula for bicyclo[3.2.1]octane illustrates the numbering.

Shortest bridge ... Longest bridge

The choice of bridge-head for position number 1 is made to permit substituents to be assigned the smaller possible position numbers.

7. Correct numbering of the formula

will assign the methyl substituent to position number ____ , while the methyl substituent in

will be assigned position number ____ .

8. Correct numbering of the formula

will assign the methyl substituent to position number ____ and the chloro substituent to position number ____ .

9. 8,8-Dichlorobicyclo[5.1.0]octane may be represented by the formula

_____.

10. 1,3-Dimethylbicyclo[1.1.0]butane may be represented by the formula

_____.

Bridged hydrocarbons containing carbon-carbon double bonds in the ring system are named by replacing the final ending ane with ene and inserting a number immediately before ene to indicate position of the alkene linkage. The bridgehead which will permit the alkene linkage to have the smaller position number is chosen for position number 1.

11. α-Pinene, the major constituent of turpentine, is 2,6,6-trimethylbicyclo[3.1.1]hept-2-ene; α-pinene may be represented by

_____ .

12. Carene, an isomer of α-pinene, may be represented by the formula

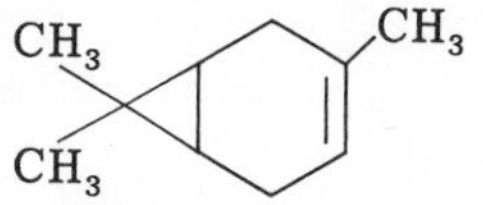

The systematic name for carene is

_____ .

13. The alkene represented by the formula

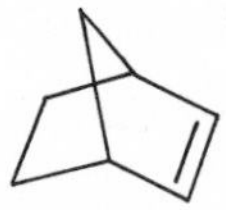

may be named with the systematic name _____ .

Bridged ring systems containing other functional groups may be named in much the same way as are bicycloalkanes; the ending ane is replaced with the appropriate systematic ending which is preceded by the smaller possible number indicating location of that functional group.

14. Camphor is a naturally occurring ketone represented by the formula

CH₃ CH₃

CH₃

O

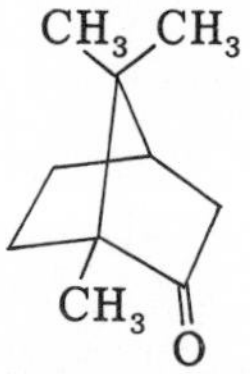

A systematic name for camphor is

_____ .

90

15. The alcohol

may be named by the systematic name _____.

16. Bicyclo[4.4.0]decane-2-carboxylic acid may be represented by the formula

_____.

HETEROCYCLIC BRIDGED SYSTEMS

Some bridged ring systems containing ring atoms other than carbon are named conveniently by the use of prefixes which signify the replacement of a carbon by the other kind of atom (usually called the hetero atom). Replacement by oxygen is signified by the operational prefix oxa, nitrogen by aza, and sulfur by thia. A number preceding the prefix and separated from it by a hyphen indicates the position of the replacement.

17. 7-Oxabicyclo[4.1.0]heptane is the name used by Chemical Abstracts for indexing the compound commonly called cyclohexene oxide and represented by the formula

_____.

18. The compound represented by the formula

may be named with the systematic name _____.

19. The name for the hydrocarbon represented by the formula

is _____; the prefix signifying replacement of carbon by nitrogen is _____; and the systematic name for the compound represented by the formula

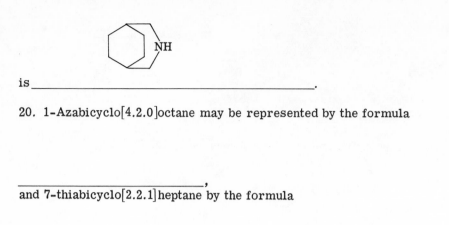

is _____.

20. 1-Azabicyclo[4.2.0]octane may be represented by the formula

_____,

and 7-thiabicyclo[2.2.1]heptane by the formula

_____.

BICYCLO[2.2.1] HEPTANE (NORBORNANE) DERIVATIVES

Derivatives of bicyclo[2.2.1]heptane are so frequently cited in the chemical literature that some special attention to nomenclature of these derivatives is appropriate. The preferred IUPAC name for 1,7,7-trimethylbicyclo[2.2.1]heptane is bornane (just as toluene is preferred over methylbenzene). In polycyclic compounds, "nor" is a prefix used to indicate that all carbons outside the ring system of the parent compound are missing; only the ring skeleton of the parent compound remains.

21. Bornane is the preferred name for the compound represented by the formula

_____,

and norbornane is the preferred name for the compound represented by the formula

_____.

Norbornane is so widely used as a name for bicyclo[2.2.1]heptane that most chemists probably do not even make a mental reference back to the parent compound, bornane, when the name norbornane appears. Numbering of positions in norbornane follows the rules for all bicycloalkanes, and substituted norbornanes are named just as other substituted hydrocarbons are.

22. The nitro substituent in the formula

is located on position number ____, and the name for the compound represented by the formula is _____.

23. 7-Chloronorbornane may be represented by the formula

_____.

24. 2-Norbornene is represented by the formula

_____,

and the unsaturated compound represented by the formula

is named _____.

25. 2-Norbornanol is represented by the formula

_____, and   is named _____.

26. 1-Methylnorbornane may be represented by the formula

_____.

The geometry of substituted norbornanes is such that a substituent in the 2 position may extend in the same general direction as the shortest bridge, or in the opposite direction. The italicized prefixes exo (same direction) and endo (opposite direction) are used to differentiate such isomers.

27. exo-2-Norbornanol may be represented by the formula

_____ ,

and endo-2-norbornanol by the formula _____ .

28. 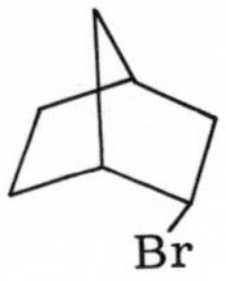 is the formula for _____ .

2-Norbornyl is the name of the alkyl group 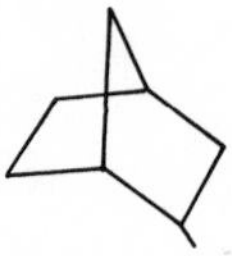 .

29. exo-2-Norbornyl acetate may be represented by the formula

_____ ,

and endo-2-norbornyl acetate by

_____ .

30. 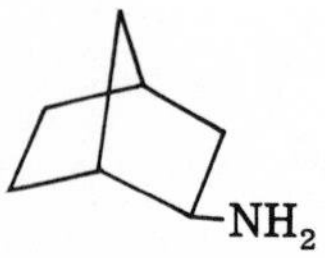 may be named _____ .

Nomenclature
of
Reaction
Intermediates

In nearly all of its stable compounds, carbon is tetravalent, but in some transient intermediates, and in a few stable compounds, carbon is trivalent or even divalent. TRIVALENT
SPECIES are called <u>carbonium ions</u>, <u>radicals</u>, and <u>carbanions</u>, which differ from each other
by the number of electrons on carbon not used in the three bonds to that carbon. These extra
electrons are often called nonbonding electrons. <u>Carbonium ions</u> have no extra electrons
(nonbonding electrons) besides those used in the three bonds between the carbon atom and
the atoms attached to it, and the ions are positively charged. <u>Radicals</u> have one unshared,
unpaired electron and are neutral. And <u>carbanions</u> have two nonbonding electrons on a carbon and are negatively charged. In structural formulas, nonbonding electrons are most often represented by dots above or beside the C (or other atomic symbol) to which they be-
long. Carbanions are often written with a negative sign instead of dots, and carbonium ions
are written with a positive sign. The $^-$ or $^+$ sign is usually written just above or beside the
trivalent carbon in the ion.

1. The unstable particle represented by the formula $CH_3 - \dot{C}H - CH_3$ has _____(number)
nonbonding electron. The particle will have ____$(+,-,0)$ charge and is classified as a _____.

2. The unstable particle represented by the formula $CH_3 - \overset{+}{C}H - CH_3$ has no nonbonding electrons and is classified as a _____.

3. A trivalent carbon with a pair of nonbonding electrons will have a ____$(+,-,0)$ charge and
will be called a _____. A carbanion composed of one C and 3H could be represented by the formula _____.

<u>Carbonium ions</u> are named by specifying the alkyl group and adding, as separate words,
<u>cation</u> or <u>carbonium ion</u>. For example, the ion represented by the formula $\overset{+}{C}H_3$ is named
<u>methyl cation</u> or <u>methyl carbonium ion</u>. "Cation" and "carbonium ion" are treated as func-

tional class names. Because "carbon" is contained in "carbonium," confusion can result if alkylcarbonium is written as one word. The name "methylcarbonium ion" has been taken to mean $CH_3-\overset{+}{C}H_2$, but "methyl carbonium ion" means only $\overset{+}{C}H_3$.

4. A name for the carbonium ion $CH_3-\overset{+}{C}H-CH_3$ is _____.

5. A name for the carbonium ion $CH_3-\underset{+}{\overset{\overset{\displaystyle CH_3}{|}}{C}}-CH_3$ is _____.

6. The t-pentyl cation may be represented by the formula _____.

7. The s-butyl cation may be represented by the formula

_____ and the isobutyl cation by the formula

_____.

8. By the terms primary, secondary, and tertiary, the s-butyl cation may be classified as a _____ carbonium ion, and the isobutyl cation may be classified as a _____ one.

9. The 1-methylcyclohexyl cation, which may be represented by the formula

_____,
will be classified as a _____ carbonium ion.

Names of specific radicals and carbanions that follow the same style used for carbonium ions are also free of ambiguity. The alkyl group name is followed by the separate word radical or anion or carbanion, as required.

10. The formula $CH_3-\overset{\cdot}{C}H-CH_3$ depicts a _____ (type of particle) which may be specifically named _____.

11. A t-butyl radical may be represented by the formula

_____ and will be classified as a _____ radical.

96

12. The formula

$$CH_3-\overset{}{\underset{\underset{CH_3}{|}}{CH}}-\bar{C}H_2$$

represents a _____ (type of particle) which may be named _____.

13. The isobutyl anion is classified as a _____ carbanion.

14. A formula for trichloromethyl anion is_____and for trichloromethyl radical is

_____.

15. The ion represented by the formula $CH_2{=}CH-\overset{+}{C}H_2$ is called
_____ and that represented by the formula $CH_2{=}\bar{C}H$ is
called _____.

16. An allyl radical may be represented by the formula _____.

17. A cyclopropylmethyl cation may be represented by the formula

_____ and classified as a _____ carbonium ion.

18. The particle represented by the formula

$$CH_3-CH_2-\overset{\cdot}{\underset{\underset{CH_2-CH_3}{|}}{C}}-CH_2-CH_3$$

is named as a substituted hydrocarbon radical. The parent chain is named _____,
and the complete name for the particle is_____.
The radical is classified as a _____ radical.

DIVALENT CARBON INTERMEDIATES are named methylenes and often called carbenes.
They are neutral particles with two nonbonding electrons, which may be paired or unpaired.
Particles with only paired electrons are described as being in the <u>singlet state</u>; those with
two unpaired electrons are described as being in the <u>triplet state</u>.

19. The ground state, or lowest energy state, for nearly all methylenes which have been
studied is the triplet state, that is, the particles contain____(number) unpaired electrons.

20. Reactions which produce methylenes often produce the excited singlet state, that is, the
methylenes at the time of generation contain____(number) unpaired electrons.

21. Under proper reaction conditions, methylenes in the excited, singlet state(___(number)

unpaired electrons) may change to the triplet, ground state (____(number) unpaired electrons) before further reaction occurs.

In addition to being a class name, methylene may specify one carbon atom and refer specifically to CH_2. Any substituents on that carbon are specified in the name just as substituents are identified in any other names. Formulas frequently include two dots for the non-bonding electrons.

22. The name of $:CH_2$ is methylene, and the name of $Cl-\ddot{C}H$ is _____.

23. The formula for dichloromethylene is _____. Extensive studies have indicated that the ground state of dichloromethylene contains no unpaired electrons, that is, the ground state of dichloromethylene is the _____ state. For most other methylenes, however, the ground state is the one with two unpaired electrons (the _____ state), and the singlet state is described as _____ (a ground or an excited) state.

24. A formula for t-butylmethylene is

_____.

The carbon structure of t-butylmethylene is related to that of the _____ (name) alkyl group.

25. Neopentylmethylene can be represented by the formula

_____.

26. A suitable name for the unstable intermediate

$$CH_3-CH_2-\underset{\underset{CH_3}{|}}{CH}-\ddot{C}-\underset{\underset{CH_3}{|}}{CH}-CH_2-CH_3$$

is _____.

Carbene has been used in names in place of methylene, but preferred usage restricts carbene to a class name. As a class name, carbene does not specify a carbon atom and is not itself modified by substitutive prefixes.

Appendix

Selected References

A Brief Summary of Some Key IUPAC Rules
for Substitutive
Names of Organic Compounds

Substitutive Name Prefixes and Suffixes
for Some
Important Functional Groups

Names of Some Important Parent Compounds
Not Specifically
Included in the Program

SELECTED REFERENCES

"Definitive Rules for Nomenclature of Organic Chemistry," 1957 Report of the Commission on the Nomenclature of Organic Chemistry, International Union of Pure and Applied Chemistry, Journal of the American Chemical Society, 82, 5545 (1960).

International Union of Pure and Applied Chemistry, Tentative Rules for Nomenclature of Organic Chemistry, 1961. London: Butterworths, 1962.

"The Naming and Indexing of Chemical Compounds from Chemical Abstracts," Introduction to Vol. 56 (January-June 1962) of Chemical Abstracts.

Cahn, R. S., An Introduction to Chemical Nomenclature, Washington, D.C.: Butterworths, 1964.

Hurd, C. D., "The General Philosophy of Organic Nomenclature," Journal of Chemical Education, 38, 43 (1961).

"Rules of Carbohydrate Nomenclature," Journal of Organic Chemistry, 28, 281 (1963).

The Ring Index, 1st ed., New York: Reinhold Publishing Co., 1940; or 2nd ed., Washington, D.C.: American Chemical Society, 1960.

Numerous reprints of IUPAC reports and ACS committee reports on specialized topics of nomenclature are available, many of them gratis, from Chemical Abstracts Service, The Ohio State University, Columbus, Ohio 43210.

A BRIEF SUMMARY OF SOME KEY IUPAC RULES
FOR SUBSTITUTIVE NAMES OF ORGANIC COMPOUNDS

1. The longest continuous chain of carbon atoms containing the functional group is the basis of the substitutive name. Atoms or groups other than hydrogen attached to the parent chain are called substituents.

2. The parent compound is named by adding the appropriate systematic ending (suffix) to the alkane name corresponding to the number of carbons in the parent chain. The final "e" in "alkane" is dropped for a suffix beginning with a vowel but is retained for a suffix beginning with a consonant.

3. Except for compounds containing multiple carbon-carbon bonds (which may be designated only by suffixes) as well as other functional groups, no parent compound names may have two systematic endings.

4. The parent chain is numbered so that the functional group which is part of the parent compound is assigned the smaller possible position number. If the parent compound is an alkane, the parent chain is numbered so that the smaller set of numbers is used to designate location of substituents.

5. Position number(s) indicating location of the functional group(s) in the parent compound usually precedes the alkane portion of the name. When the systematic ending clearly requires that the functional group include the terminal carbon of the parent chain (for example, -al for aldehyde), the position number 1 is omitted from the name.

6. A position number for each substituent must appear in the name even when the same number must be used more than once for the same kind of substituent. The position number immediately precedes the substituent name to which it applies in the name of the compound.

7. Position numbers occurring together in the name are separated from each other by commas, and all position numbers are separated from the rest of the name by hyphens.

8. The position by which an alkyl group substituent is attached to a parent chain is always designated position number 1, but the number 1 never appears in the name of the alkyl group. Position numbers are used to indicate location of substituents in the alkyl group, even if the substituents are other alkyl groups and are on position number 1. For example, s-butyl, $CH_3-CH_2-CH-CH_3$, may also be named 1-methylpropyl but not 2-butyl.

SUBSTITUTIVE NAME PREFIXES AND SUFFIXES
FOR SOME IMPORTANT FUNCTIONAL GROUPS

Class	Formula[a]	Prefix[b]	Suffix[c]
Acid halides	$-CO-Hal$	Haloformyl or halocarbonyl	-carbonyl halide
	$-(C)O-Hal$	—	-oyl halide
Alcohols	$-OH$	Hydroxy	-ol
Aldehydes	$-CHO$	Formyl	-carbaldehyde or -carboxaldehyde
	$-(C)HO$	Oxo	-al
Alkenes	$-(C=C)-$	—	-ene
Alkynes	$-(C\equiv C)-$	—	-yne
Amides	$-CO-NH_2$	Carbamoyl	-carboxamide
	$-(C)O-NH_2$	—	-amide
Carboxylic acids	$-COOH$	Carboxy	-carboxylic acid
	$-(C)OOH$	—	-oic acid
Esters	$-COOR$	Alkyloxycarbonyl	Alkyl ...-carboxylate
	$-(C)OOR$	—	Alkyl ...-oate
Ethers	$-OR$	Alkyloxy	—
Ketones	$>(C)=O$	Oxo	-one
Nitriles	$-C\equiv N$	Cyano	-carbonitrile
	$-(C)\equiv N$	—	-nitrile
Phenols	$-OH$	Hydroxy	-ol
Sulfides	$-SR$	Alkylthio	—
Sulfonic acids	$-SO_3H$	Sulfo	-sulfonic acid
Thiols	$-SH$	Mercapto	-thiol

[a] Carbon atoms in parentheses are included in the name of the parent chain and not in the prefix fix or suffix.

[b] Functional group is treated as a substituent.

[c] Functional group is part of the parent compound.

NAMES OF SOME IMPORTANT PARENT COMPOUNDS
NOT SPECIFICALLY INCLUDED IN THE PROGRAM

The rules of nomenclature included in this program are readily applied to substituted compounds based on these parent compounds.

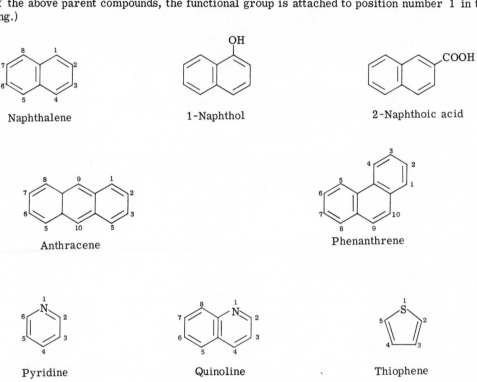

| Phenol | Aniline | Benzoic acid | Benzaldehyde | Acetophenone |

(In each of the above parent compounds, the functional group is attached to position number 1 in the benzene ring.)

| Naphthalene | 1-Naphthol | 2-Naphthoic acid |

| Anthracene | Phenanthrene |

| Pyridine | Quinoline | Thiophene |

Answer Sheets

IMPORTANT NOTE

Remove the answer sheet for the chapter being studied by tearing it from the book along the perforated line. Cover the answers with an index card or a sheet of paper, and, <u>after</u> you have written your answer in the appropriate blank, expose the answers one at a time to check your response.

1.
$$H-\underset{\underset{H}{|}}{\overset{\overset{H}{|}}{C}}-\underset{\underset{H}{|}}{\overset{\overset{H}{|}}{C}}-\underset{\underset{H}{|}}{\overset{\overset{H}{|}}{C}}-H$$

2. four
one

3. $CH_3-CH_2-CH_3$

4. four
four

5. meth
ane

6. ethane
propane

7. $CH_3-CH_2-CH_2-CH_3$ (or $CH_3-\overset{\overset{\displaystyle CH_3}{|}}{CH}-CH_3$)

8. alkane

9. seven

10. $CH_3-CH_2-CH-\overset{}{CH}-CH_2-CH_3$
     $\underset{}{CH_3}\ \ \overset{|}{CH}-CH_2-CH_3$
     $\underset{}{CH_3}$

11. hept
heptane

12. three

13. one
methyl
two
ethyl

14. methyl
methyl
ethyl

15. dimethyl

16. dimethylethylheptane

17. eleven
eleven
seven
one
one
two
eleven

18. 3, 4, 5

19. 3,5-dimethyl-4-ethylheptane

20. the longest continuous chain of carbon atoms, or the parent chain, or the chain of carbon atoms serving as a basis of the name.
substituents

three
positions of substituents along the parent (longest continuous) chain
commas
hyphens

21. longest continuous
carbon atoms
seven
hept
heptane
three
methyl, ethyl, ethyl

22. 2, 3, 5
3, 5, 6
2, 3, 5
2; 3 and 5
commas; hyphens

23. 2-methyl-3,5-diethylheptane

24. five
pentane
2,2,4-trimethylpentane

25. 5,5-diethyldecane

26. $CH_3-CH_2-\overset{\overset{\displaystyle CH_3}{|}}{\underset{\underset{\displaystyle CH_3-CH_2}{|}}{C}}-\overset{}{\underset{\underset{\displaystyle CH_3}{|}}{CH}}-CH_2-CH_3$

27. $CH_3-\overset{\overset{\displaystyle CH_3}{|}}{CH}-CH_2-\overset{\overset{\displaystyle CH_3}{|}}{CH}-\overset{\overset{\displaystyle CH_3}{|}}{CH}-CH_2-CH_2-CH_3$

28. C_6H_{14}
C_6H_{14}
isomers

29. $CH_3-CH_2-CH_2-CH_2-CH_3$
$CH_3-\overset{\overset{\displaystyle CH_3}{|}}{CH}-CH_2-CH_3$
$CH_3-\overset{\overset{\displaystyle CH_3}{|}}{\underset{\underset{\displaystyle CH_3}{|}}{C}}-CH_3$

30. four
one

31. pentane
2-methylbutane
2,2-dimethylpropane

32. $CH_3-CH_2-CH_2-CH_3$
$CH_3-\overset{\overset{\displaystyle CH_3}{|}}{CH}-CH_3$

33. pent
    5
    iso
    isopentane

34. hexane
    isohexane

35. 3-methylpentane

36. $CH_3-CH_2-CH_2-CH_2-CH_3$

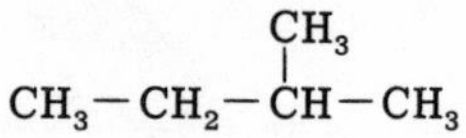

$$CH_3-CH_2-\overset{\displaystyle CH_3}{\underset{\displaystyle |}{CH}}-CH_3$$

37. 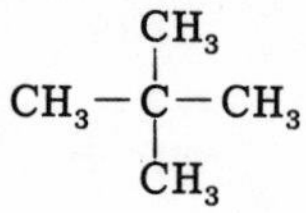 $CH_3-\overset{\displaystyle CH_3}{\underset{\displaystyle \underset{\displaystyle CH_3}{|}}{\overset{|}{C}}}-CH_3$

38. neopentane

39. neohexane

40. 2,3,3-trimethylhexane

41. C_4H_8

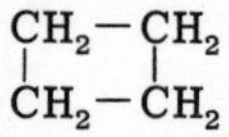

$$\begin{array}{c} CH_2-CH_2 \\ |\qquad\ | \\ CH_2-CH_2 \end{array}$$

    cyclobutane

42. cyclohexane

43. ethylcyclopentane

44. 1-methyl-3-ethylcyclohexane
    <u>or</u> 1-ethyl-3-methylcyclohexane

45. 1,3-dimethylcyclobutane

1. methyl
   ethyl

2. but
   butyl

3. pent
   pentyl

4. $CH_3-CH_2-CH_2-CH_2-$

   primary

5. secondary

6. primary
   tertiary

7. primary

8. $CH_3-CH_2-\underset{\underset{\displaystyle CH_3}{|}}{CH}-CH_3$

9. $CH_3-\underset{\underset{\displaystyle CH_3}{|}}{\overset{\overset{\displaystyle CH_3}{|}}{C}}-$

   $\underline{t}$-butyl or $\underline{tert}$-butyl

10. $\underline{t}$-pentyl or $\underline{tert}$-pentyl

11. $CH_3-\underset{\underset{\displaystyle CH_3}{|}}{CH}-CH_2$

    $CH_3-\underset{\underset{\displaystyle CH_3}{|}}{CH}-CH_2-$

    primary

12. $CH_3-\underset{\underset{\displaystyle CH_3}{|}}{CH}-CH_2-CH_3$

    $CH_3-\underset{\underset{\displaystyle CH_3}{|}}{CH}-CH_2-CH_2-$

    primary

13. isohexyl

14. $CH_3-\underset{\underset{\displaystyle CH_3}{|}}{\overset{\overset{\displaystyle CH_3}{|}}{C}}-CH_3$

    $CH_3-\underset{\underset{\displaystyle CH_3}{|}}{\overset{\overset{\displaystyle CH_3}{|}}{C}}-CH_2-$

15. continuous $\underline{or}$ unbranched
    branched

16. $CH_3-CH_2-\underset{|}{CH}-CH_3$

17. $CH_3-\underset{\underset{\displaystyle CH_3}{|}}{CH}-CH_2-$

18. primary
    secondary

19. secondary
    isopropyl

20. isopropyl
    isopropylcyclobutane

21. 10
    methyl and $\underline{s}$-butyl (or $\underline{sec}$-butyl)
    2 and 5
    2-methyl-5-$\underline{s}$-butyldecane

22. 10
    isobutyl
    5
    decane
    5-isobutyldecane

23. isopropyl chloride
    2-chloropropane

24. $CH_3-\underset{\underset{\displaystyle CH_3}{|}}{CH}-CH_2-Cl$

    $CH_3-CH_2-\underset{\underset{\displaystyle Cl}{|}}{CH}-CH_3$

    $CH_3-\underset{\underset{\displaystyle CH_3}{|}}{\overset{\overset{\displaystyle CH_3}{|}}{C}}-Cl$

25. $CH_3-\underset{\underset{\displaystyle CH_3}{|}}{\overset{\overset{\displaystyle CH_3}{|}}{C}}-CH_2-Cl$

    1-chloro-2,2-dimethylpropane
    primary

26. 1-chloro-3-methylbutane
    isopentyl chloride
    primary

27. pentane
    5
    C—C—C—C—C
    3
    2,2 and 4

    1   2   3   4   5
    C—C—C—C—C

$$\begin{array}{c}
\overset{\displaystyle CH_3}{\vert} \\
C-C-C-C-C \\
\underset{\displaystyle CH_3}{\vert}\ \underset{\displaystyle CH_3}{\vert}
\end{array}$$

$$\begin{array}{c}
\overset{\displaystyle CH_3}{\vert} \\
CH_3-C-CH_2-CH-CH_3 \\
\underset{\displaystyle CH_3}{\vert}\underset{\displaystyle CH_3}{\vert}
\end{array}$$

28.
$$\begin{array}{c}
\overset{\displaystyle CH_3}{\vert}\ \overset{\displaystyle Cl}{\vert}\ \overset{\displaystyle CH_3}{\vert} \\
CH_3-CH-C-CH-CH_2-CH_2-CH_3 \\
\underset{\displaystyle CH-CH_3}{\vert} \\
\underset{\displaystyle CH_3}{\vert}
\end{array}$$

29.
$$\begin{array}{c}
CH_3-CH-CH_2-CH_2-CH_3 \\
\underset{\displaystyle Cl}{\vert}
\end{array}$$

$$\begin{array}{c}
CH_3-CH_2-CH-CH_2-CH_3 \\
\underset{\displaystyle Cl}{\vert}
\end{array}$$

$$\begin{array}{c}
CH_3-CH-CH-CH_3 \\
\underset{\displaystyle Cl}{\vert}\ \underset{\displaystyle CH_3}{\vert}
\end{array}$$

30.
$$\begin{array}{c}
\overset{\displaystyle Cl}{\vert} \\
CH_3-C-CH_2-CH_2-CH_3 \\
\underset{\displaystyle CH_3}{\vert}
\end{array}$$

$$\begin{array}{c}
\overset{\displaystyle Cl}{\vert} \\
CH_3-CH_2-C-CH_2-CH_3 \\
\underset{\displaystyle CH_3}{\vert}
\end{array}$$

$$\begin{array}{c}
\overset{\displaystyle Cl}{\vert}\ \overset{\displaystyle CH_3}{\vert} \\
CH_3-C-CH-CH_3 \\
\underset{\displaystyle CH_3}{\vert}
\end{array}$$

31. 2-chloro-3-methylbutane

32.
$$\begin{array}{c}
\overset{\displaystyle Cl}{\vert}\ \overset{\displaystyle CH_3}{\vert} \\
CH_3-C-CH-CH_3 \\
\underset{\displaystyle CH_3}{\vert}
\end{array}$$

33. 5
3
1,1-diethyl-4-methypentyl

34. 1-isopropylbutyl
1-isopropylbutylcycloheptane

35.
$$\begin{array}{c}
CH_3-CH_2-CH_2-CH-CH_2-CH-CH_2-CH_2-CH_2-CH_3 \\
\underset{\displaystyle Cl}{\vert}\underset{\displaystyle CH_2-CH-CH_2-CH_3}{\vert} \\
\underset{\displaystyle CH_2-CH_3}{\vert}
\end{array}$$

36. s-butyl
1,1-dimethyl-3-chloropentyl
1-s-butyl-4-(1,1-dimethyl-3-chloropentyl)-
    cyclooctane

110

1. seven

2. heptene

3. s-butyl

4. 2
   3

5. 2-heptene

6. 3-s-butyl-2-heptene

7. hexene

8. 1
   3, 5, 5

9. that numbering would incorrectly assign a higher number (5) to the functional group (C=C), which must have the smaller possible number.

10. 3,5,5-trimethyl-1-hexene

11. $CH_3-CH_2-CH=CH_2$, $CH_3-CH=CH-CH_3$,

    and $CH_3-C=CH_2$
    $\qquad\qquad\ \ |$
    $\qquad\qquad\ CH_3$

12. 1-butene, 2-butene, and methylpropene (number unnecessary because substituent methyl cannot be on any other carbon if basis of name is to be propene).

13.

14. cyclooctene

15. $CH_3-\overset{\overset{\textstyle CH_3}{|}}{\underset{\underset{\textstyle CH_3}{|}}{C}}$ (cyclohexene ring)

16. (cyclopentene ring) $-\overset{}{\underset{\underset{\textstyle CH_3}{|}}{CH}}-CH_2-CH_3$

17. 3-chloropropene (3-chloro-1-propene)

18. 1-chloro-2-isobutylcyclobutene

19. 1 and 5
    2 and 3
    1 and 5
    1-chloro-5-methylcyclopentene

20. 3,4,4,5,6 and 3,4,5,5,6
    3,4,4,5,6
    3,5-dichloro-4,4,6-trimethylcyclohexene

21. propylene

22. branched
    $CH_3-\overset{\overset{}{}}{\underset{\underset{\textstyle CH_3}{|}}{C}}=CH_2$

23. allyl chloride
    vinyl chloride

24. (cyclohexane ring)$-CH=CH_2$

25. (bicyclic ring)$-CH_2-CH=CH_2$

26. $CH_3-CH_2-CH=CH_2$, $CH_3-CH=CH-CH_3$,
    and $CH_3-\overset{\overset{}{}}{\underset{\underset{\textstyle CH_3}{|}}{C}}=CH_2$

27. one
    2-butene

28. $\overset{\textstyle CH_3}{\diagdown}\!\!\!\overset{\textstyle CH_3}{\diagup}$ and $\overset{\textstyle CH_3}{\diagdown}\!\!\!\overset{\textstyle H}{\diagup}$
    C=C   C=C
    $\overset{\textstyle H}{\diagup}\!\!\!\overset{\textstyle H}{\diagdown}$ $\overset{\textstyle H}{\diagup}\!\!\!\overset{\textstyle CH_3}{\diagdown}$

29. $\overset{\textstyle CH_3}{\diagdown}\!\!\!\overset{\textstyle CH_3}{\diagup}$
    C=C
    $\overset{\textstyle H}{\diagup}\!\!\!\overset{\textstyle H}{\diagdown}$

30. $\overset{\textstyle Cl}{\diagdown}\!\!\!\overset{\textstyle H}{\diagup}$
    C=C
    $\overset{\textstyle H}{\diagup}\!\!\!\overset{\textstyle Cl}{\diagdown}$

31. trans-2-butene

32. like groups or atoms are on opposite sides of the alkene linkage

33. 5-methyl-cis-2-hexene

34. $CH_3-\overset{}{\underset{\underset{\textstyle CH_3}{|}}{CH}}-CH_2-CH_2-CH_2-CH_2-\overset{\overset{\textstyle Cl}{|}}{C}=\overset{}{\underset{\underset{\textstyle Cl}{|}}{C}}-CH_2-CH_3$

35.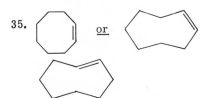

36. trans
    10
    trans-cyclodecene

111

37. cyclopropane
2
cis
1, 2
<u>cis</u>-1,2-dimethylcyclopropane

38. cyclopentane

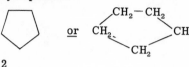

2
isopropyl

CH_3-CH-
      |
     CH_3

1, 3
the two substituents extend in the same direction with respect to the general plane of the ring.

CH_3-CH $CH-CH_3$
      | |
     CH_3 CH_3

39. $CH_3-CH-CH_2$
        |
      CH_3 Cl

40. chlorine
ethylene

41. isobutylene chloride

42. 1,2-dichloro-2-methylpropane

43. CH_2I_2

44. $Cl-CH_2-CH_2-CH_2-Cl$

45. propylene glycol
trimethylene glycol

          CH_3
          |
46. CH_3-C-CH_2
         | |
        OH OH

$HO-CH_2-CH_2-CH_2-CH_2-OH$

47. $Cl-CH_2-CH_2-OH$ <u>or</u> CH_2-CH_2
                             | |
                            Cl   OH

propylene chlorohydrin

48. $CH_3-CH-CH_2$
           _O_/

49. isobutylene oxide

50. epoxy
6
3 and 4
3,4-epoxyhexane

51. 1-chloro-3,4-epoxy-5-<u>s</u>-butylnonane

52. cyclohexene
cyclohexene oxide

53. ☐—OH
     |
    —OH

54. <u>trans</u>-cyclooctene
<u>trans</u>-cyclooctene oxide

55. $CH_2=CH-CH_2-CH=CH_2$

$CH_2=CH-CH=CH-CH_3$

56. 1,3-butadiene

57. $CH_2=C-CH=CH_2$
      |
    CH_3

58. $CH_2=C=CH_2$

59. $CH_2=C=CH_2$
1,2-butadiene

60.

61. conjugated

62. isolated

63. $CH_2=C=CH_2$
cumulated

64. $CH_3-CH-CH=CH-C=CH-CH_2-CH_2-CH_2-CH_3$
        | |
       Cl CH_2-CH_3

conjugated

CHAPTER 4   ALCOHOLS

1. isopropyl alcohol

2. $CH_3-\underset{\underset{OH}{|}}{CH}-CH_2-CH_3$

3. alcohol is a class name rather than the name of a specific compound.

4. isopentyl
   isopentyl alcohol

5. allyl
   allyl alcohol

6. $CH_3-\underset{\underset{CH_3}{|}}{\overset{\overset{CH_3}{|}}{C}}-OH$

7. CH_3-CH_2-OH
   primary

8. $CH_3-\underset{\underset{CH_3}{|}}{CH}-CH_2-OH$
   primary

9. primary

10. the OH group is attached to a primary carbon; that is, to a carbon which is attached to only one other carbon.

11. secondary

12. $CH_3-\underset{\underset{OH}{|}}{CH}-CH_2-CH_3$
    s-butyl alcohol

13. $CH_3-\underset{\underset{OH}{|}}{CH}-CH_2-CH_2-CH_3$,

    $CH_3-CH_2-\underset{\underset{OH}{|}}{CH}-CH_2-CH_3$,

    $CH_3-\underset{\underset{CH_3}{|}}{CH}-\overset{\overset{OH}{|}}{CH}-CH_3$

14. $CH_3-\underset{\underset{CH_3}{|}}{\overset{\overset{CH_3}{|}}{C}}-OH$
    t-butyl alcohol

15. 3-pentanol

16. $CH_3-\underset{\underset{OH}{|}}{CH}-CH_2-CH_3$

17. cyclohexanol

18. 3-methyl-2-butanol

19. 9
    nonane

20. nonanol

21. 4
    4-nonanol

22. 3
    chloro, methyl, and isopropyl
    3, 4, and 6

23. hyphens
    commas

24. 3-chloro-4-methyl-6-isopropyl-4-nonanol

25. tertiary

26. chlorohydrin

27. hypochlorous acid (HOCl)
    alkenes
    HOCl

    $CH_3-CH_2-CH=\overset{\overset{CH_3}{|}}{C}-CH_2-\underset{\underset{\underset{\underset{CH_3}{|}}{CH-CH_3}}{|}}{CH}-CH_2-CH_2-CH_3$

28. $CH_3-CH_2-\underset{\underset{CH_2-CH_3}{|}}{\overset{\overset{OH}{|}}{C}}-CH_2-CH_3$
    triethylcarbinol

29. cyclopropylcarbinol
    cyclopropylmethanol

30. diethyl-s-butylcarbinol
    3-ethyl-4-methyl-3-hexanol
       (or 4-methyl-3-ethyl-3-hexanol)
    tertiary

31. $CH_3-\underset{\underset{CH_3}{|}}{\overset{\overset{OH}{|}}{C}}-CH_2-OH$
    2-methyl-1,2-propanediol

32. 2,4
    lower possible
    5,6,6-trimethyl-2,4-heptanediol

33. $CH_2{=}CH{-}CH_2{-}OH$
2-propen-1-ol

34. 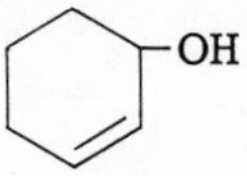 OH

35. 4-cycloocten-1-ol

36. 7
heptenol
3, 5
5-hepten-3-ol
2
methyl, ethyl
6, 4
6-methyl-4-ethyl-5-hepten-3-ol

37. $CH_3{-}\underset{\underset{OH}{|}}{CH}{-}\underset{\underset{CH_3}{|}}{C}{=}CH{-}\underset{\underset{Cl}{|}}{CH}{-}CH_3$

38. 6-methyl-3-heptene-2,5-diol

39. 4-s-butyl-4-cyclohexene-1,2-diol

40.

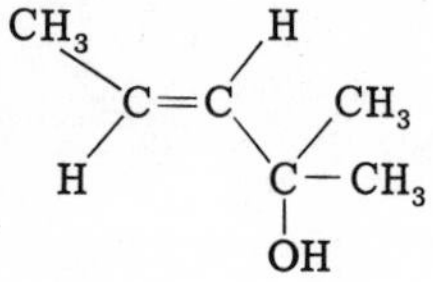

41. 2-methyl-6-ethyl-cis-3-decen-1-ol

42. 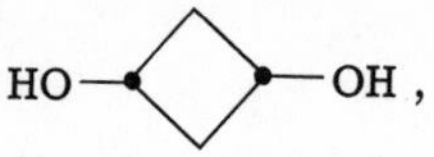 HO—◇—OH ,

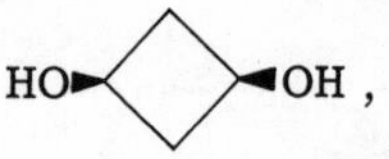

HO►◇◄OH ,

and HO◇OH

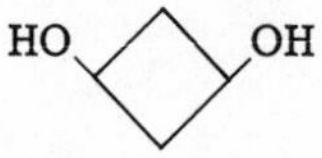

43. $CH_2{=}CH{-}$

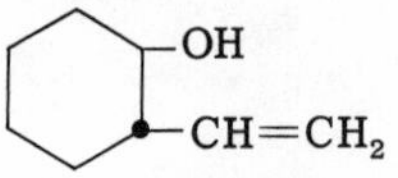

OH
$CH{=}CH_2$

or OH
$CH{=}CH_2$

or OH
$CH{=}CH_2$

114

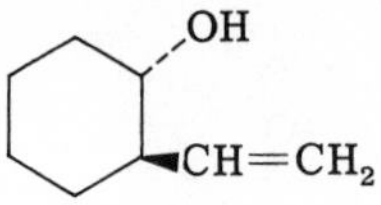

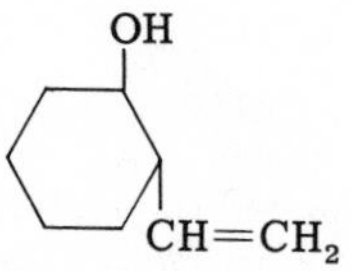

1. propyne

2. 7
   hept
   yne
   heptyne
   3
   3-heptyne
   methyl, ethyl
   2, 5
   2-methyl-5-ethyl-3-heptyne

3. 2-butyne

4. $CH_3-CH_2-C\equiv C-CH_2-CH_3$

5. 8
   oct
   $C\equiv C$
   $C-C\equiv C-C-C-C-C-C$
   Cl

   $CH_3-CH_2-\underset{\underset{CH_3}{|}}{CH}-$

   $\underset{\underset{Cl}{|}}{CH_2}-C\equiv C-\underset{\underset{\underset{CH_3}{|}}{CH-CH_2-CH_3}}{CH}-CH_2-CH_2-CH_2-CH_3$

6. ethylacetylene
   diethylacetylene

7. the final portion of the name is the name of an individual compound.

8. $C\equiv C$
   methyl, isobutyl
   CH_3- and $CH_3-\underset{\underset{CH_3}{|}}{CH}-CH_2-$

$CH_3-C\equiv C-CH_2-\underset{\underset{CH_3}{|}}{CH}-CH_3$

9. 5-methyl-2-hexyne

10. vinyl
    vinylacetylene

11. vinylisopropylacetylene
    (or isopropylvinylacetylene)

12. $HC\equiv C-CH=CH_2$
    butenyne (no numbers because there are no isomeric butenynes)

13. $HC\equiv C-CH_2-CH=CH_2$
    1-penten-4-yne

14. 4-chloro-7-isopropyl-6-nonen-2-yne

15. OH
    $C=C$
    ol

16. 4-penten-2-ol

17. 4-pentyn-2-ol

18. $HC\equiv C-\underset{\underset{OH}{|}}{\overset{\overset{CH_3}{|}}{C}}-CH_2-CH_3$

19. ethynyl
    8
    3
    5, 6, 6
    6,6-dimethyl-5-ethynyl-3-octanol

20.

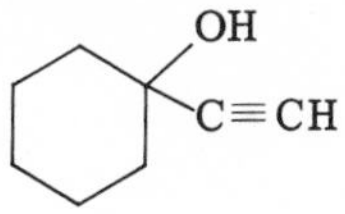

1. methyl ethyl ether

2. ethyl ether

3. $CH_3-O-\overset{\displaystyle CH_3}{\underset{\displaystyle CH_3}{\overset{|}{\underset{|}{C}}}}-CH_3$

4. $CH_2=CH-$
    $CH_3-O-CH=CH_2$

5. pent
    isopentyl
    allyl
    allyl isopentyl ether

6. s-butyl
    s-butyl ether

7. the ending ether implies two alkyl groups;
    if both are the same, one name of the alkyl
    group is sufficient.

8. t-pentyl
    cyclopropyl
    cyclopropyl t-pentyl ether

9. $CH_3-O-\overset{\displaystyle }{\underset{\displaystyle CH_3}{\overset{|}{\underset{|}{CH}}}}-CH_3$

    propane
    2
    methoxy
    2-methoxypropane

10. 7
    heptane
    2, 3, and 5
    ethoxy
    2,3-dimethyl-5-ethoxyheptane

11. $CH_3-O-CH_2-CH=CH-\overset{\displaystyle }{\underset{\displaystyle O-CH_3}{\overset{|}{\underset{|}{CH}}}}-CH_3$

12. $CH_3-\overset{\displaystyle }{\underset{\displaystyle CH_3}{\overset{|}{\underset{|}{CH}}}}-CH_2-O-CH_2-\overset{\displaystyle H}{\underset{\displaystyle H}{\overset{|}{\underset{|}{C}}}}=\overset{\displaystyle }{\underset{\displaystyle CH_3}{\overset{|}{\underset{|}{C}}}}-CH-O-CH_2-\overset{\displaystyle }{\underset{\displaystyle CH_3}{\overset{|}{\underset{|}{CH}}}}-CH_3$

13. (chloromethoxy)methane
        (or methoxychloromethane)
    methyl chloromethyl ether
    two identical alkyl groups (two $ClCH_2-$
        groups)

14. $Cl-CH_2-O-CH_2-Cl$

15. cyclohexanol
    ethoxy, chloromethyl
    1
    5
    2-chloromethyl-5-ethoxy-1-cyclohexanol
        (or 2-chloromethyl-5-ethoxycyclohexanol)

16. 10
    decyne
    2
    isopropoxy
    5
    5-isopropoxy-2-decyne

1. prop
   propion
   but
   butyr

2. CH_3-COOH
   acetic acid

3. 2

4. chloroacetic acid
   trichloroacetic acid

5.
$$CH_3-\overset{\overset{\displaystyle CH_3}{|}}{\underset{\underset{\displaystyle CH_3}{|}}{C}}-O-$$

$$CH_3-\overset{\overset{\displaystyle CH_3}{|}}{\underset{\underset{\displaystyle CH_3}{|}}{C}}-O-CH_2-COOH$$

6.
$$CH_3-\underset{\underset{\displaystyle Cl}{|}}{CH}-COOH$$

$$\underset{\underset{\displaystyle Cl}{|}}{CH_2}-CH_2-COOH$$

7. hydroxy
   valeric acid
   γ-hydroxyvaleric acid or 4-hydroxyvaleric
   acid

8. 5
   omega or ω
   ω-bromovaleric acid

9. ethanoic acid
   pentanoic acid

10. $CH_3-CH_2-CH_2-COOH$

11. 6
    hex
    hexanoic acid
    3
    3-methylhexanoic acid

12. 7
    3,3 and 5
    3-chloro-3-ethyl-5-methylheptanoic acid

13. $H-C\equiv C-$
    CH_3-CH_2-O-

$$CH_3-CH_2-O-CH_2-CH_2-CH_2-\overset{\overset{\displaystyle HC\equiv C}{|}}{CH}-COOH$$

14. 1

15. 2-butenoic acid

16. $CH_2=CH-CH_2-CH_2-CH_2-CH_2-CH_2-CH_2-CH_2-COOH$ or $CH_2=CH-(CH_2)_7-COOH$ 117

17. 2-butynoic acid
    4-hexynoic acid

18. 2-chloro-4-hexenoic acid

19. 2-bromo-4-ethoxy-6-isopropyl-7-nonynoic
    acid

20. alkenoic
    alkynoic

21.
$$\underset{H}{\overset{CH_3}{>}}C=C\underset{CH-COOH}{\overset{H}{<}}$$
$$CH_3-CH_2$$

$$\underset{H}{\overset{CH_3}{>}}C=C\underset{\overset{CH-COOH}{CH_2-CH_3}}{\overset{}{<}}$$
$$H$$

22.
$$CH_3-\overset{\overset{\displaystyle CH_3}{|}}{\underset{\underset{\displaystyle CH_3}{|}}{C}}-COOH$$

    2,2-dimethylpropanoic acid

23. diisopropylacetic acid
    3-methyl-2-isopropylbutanoic acid

24.
$$CH_3-\overset{\overset{\displaystyle CH_3}{|}}{\underset{\underset{\displaystyle CH_3}{|}}{C}}-CH_2-$$

$$CH_3-\overset{\overset{\displaystyle CH_3}{|}}{\underset{\underset{\displaystyle CH_3}{|}}{C}}-CH_2-CH_2-COOH$$

25. $\triangleright-COOH$

26. vinyl, hydroxy
    4, 3
    3-hydroxy-4-vinylcyclohexanecarboxylic
    acid

27. cis
    1, 3
    cis-3-chlorocyclopentanecarboxylic acid

1. acetic acid
   acet
   acetyl chloride

2. hexanoic acid
   hexanoyl chloride

3. $CH_3-CH-COOH$
   $\quad\quad\quad |$
   $\quad\quad\quad Br$

   $CH_3-CH-CO-Br$
   $\quad\quad\quad |$
   $\quad\quad\quad Br$

   2-bromopropanoyl bromide

4. $-CH-CO-Cl$

5. 18
   stearoyl chloride

6. acetic acid
   acetic anhydride

7. $\quad\quad CH_3$
   $\quad\quad\quad |$
   $CH_3-C-COOH$
   $\quad\quad\quad |$
   $\quad\quad CH_3$

   or $(CH_3)_3C-COOH$

   $\quad\quad CH_3\quad\quad\quad CH_3$
   $\quad\quad\quad |\quad\quad\quad\quad\quad |$
   $CH_3-C-CO-O-CO-C-CH_3$
   $\quad\quad\quad |\quad\quad\quad\quad\quad |$
   $\quad\quad CH_3\quad\quad\quad CH_3$

   or $(CH_3)_3C-CO-O-CO-C(CH_3)_3$

8. formic acid
   propionic acid
   formic propionic anhydride

9. acetic isovaleric anhydride

10. $CH_3-CH_2-CH_2-CH_2-CH_2-CH-\overset{\overset{\displaystyle O}{\|}}{C}-O-\overset{\overset{\displaystyle O}{\|}}{C}-CH_2-CH_2-CH-CH_2-CH_3$
    $\quad\quad\quad\quad\quad\quad\quad\quad\quad\quad\quad\quad |\quad\quad\quad\quad\quad\quad\quad\quad\quad\quad\quad\quad\quad |$
    $\quad\quad\quad\quad\quad\quad\quad\quad\quad\quad\quad\quad CH_2\quad\quad\quad\quad\quad\quad\quad\quad\quad\quad\quad CH_3$
    $\quad\quad\quad\quad\quad\quad\quad\quad\quad\quad\quad\quad |$
    $\quad\quad\quad\quad\quad\quad\quad\quad\quad\quad\quad\quad CH_3$

11. formic acid
    methanoate
    formate

12. propanoic acid
    propionate
    propanoate

13. butyrate

14. methyl butyrate

15. s-butyl
    cyclopentanecarboxylic acid
    cyclopentanecarboxylate
    s-butyl cyclopentanecarboxylate

16. CF_3-COOH

    $CH_3-CH-CH_2-$
    $\quad\quad\quad |$
    $\quad\quad CH_3$

    $CF_3-COO-CH_2-CH-CH_3$
    $\quad\quad\quad\quad\quad\quad\quad\quad\quad |$
    $\quad\quad\quad\quad\quad\quad\quad\quad CH_3$

17. $CH_3-CH-COOH$
    $\quad\quad\quad |$
    $\quad\quad CH_3$

    $CH_3-CH-COO-CH_2-CH-CH_3$
    $\quad\quad\quad |\quad\quad\quad\quad\quad\quad\quad\quad |$
    $\quad\quad CH_3\quad\quad\quad\quad\quad CH_3$

18. allyl formate

19. $CH_2{=}CH-CH_2-O-\overset{\overset{\displaystyle O}{\|}}{C}-CH_2-CH_3$

    $CH_2{=}CH-O-\overset{\overset{\displaystyle O}{\|}}{C}-CH_3$

20. 5
    2, 4
    methoxy, methyl
    4-methyl-2-methoxypentyl
    7
    5
    3
    5-chloro-3-methyl-5-heptenoic acid
    5-chloro-3-methyl-5-heptenoate
    4-methyl-2-methoxypentyl 5-chloro-
       3-methyl-5-heptenoate

21. 2-chloro-4-methylcyclohexyl
    2-chloro-4-methylcyclohexyl acetate

22. $CH_3-CH_2\quad\quad\quad H$
    $\quad\quad\quad\quad\quad\diagdown\;\diagup$
    $\quad\quad\quad\quad\quad\quad C{=}C$
    $\quad\quad\quad\quad\quad\diagup\;\diagdown$
    $\quad\quad\quad\quad H\quad\quad\quad\quad CH_2-O-CO-CH_3$

23. 3-cyclooctenyl formate

24. 18
    $CH_3-(CH_2)_{16}-COOH$

    $CH_3-(CH_2)_{16}-\overset{\overset{\displaystyle O}{\|}}{C}-O-CH_3$

1. a ketone

2. an aldehyde

3. an aldehyde
   a ketone

4. pentane
   pentanal

5. propanone

6. =O

7. CH_3-CH_2-CHO

8. $CH_3-CH_2-CH_2-CO-CH_3$
   $CH_3-CH_2-CO-CH_2-CH_3$
   2-pentanone
   3-pentanone

9. $CH_3-CH_2-\underset{\underset{Cl}{|}}{CH}-CO-CH_3$

   $CH_3-CH_2-\underset{\underset{Cl}{|}}{CH}-CH_2-CHO$

10. 5-methyl-2-hexene
    5-methyl-2-hexenal

11. 2-methyl-2-heptene
    1
    5
    6
    6-methyl-5-heptenal

12. $CH_3-CH_2-CO-CH_2-CH_2-\underset{\underset{CH_2=CH}{|}}{CH}-CH_2-\underset{\underset{O-\underset{\underset{CH_3}{|}}{CH}-CH_3}{|}}{CH}-CH_3$

13. Cyclopentanecarboxaldehyde (<u>or</u> cyclopentanecarbaldehyde)

14. 3-methylcyclobutanecarboxaldehyde (<u>or</u> 3-methylcyclobutanecarbaldehyde)

15. CH_3––CHO <u>or</u> CH_3CHO <u>or</u> CHO

16. $CH_3-CO-CH_2-COOH$

17. $H-\underset{\underset{O}{\|}}{C}-CH_2-CH_2-CH_2-CH_2-COOH$

    an aldehyde

18. $CH_3-\underset{\underset{O}{\|}}{C}-CH_2-CH_2-CH_2-CH_2-CH_2-\underset{\underset{H}{|}}{\overset{\overset{H}{|}}{C}}=C-COOH$

19. vinyl
    oxo
    3,6-dimethyl-5-oxoheptanoic acid
    vinyl 3,6-dimethyl-5-oxoheptanoate

20. cyclodecenecarboxaldehyde
    (<u>or</u> cyclodecenecarbaldehyde)
    2
    7-oxo-2-cyclodecenecarboxaldehyde
    (<u>or</u> 7-oxo-2-cyclodecenecarbaldehyde)

21. acetaldehyde

22. propionaldehyde
    isovaleraldehyde

23. $CH_3-\underset{\underset{CH_3}{|}}{CH}-CHO$

24. 1   methan   methanal
    2   ethan   ethanal
    5   pentan   pentanal

25. $CH_3-\underset{\underset{Cl}{|}}{CH}-CHO$

26. β-hydroxybutyraldehyde
    (<u>or</u> 3-hydroxybutyraldehyde)
    3-hydroxybutanal

27. β and γ

28. $CH_3-\underset{\underset{Br}{|}}{CH}-CH_2-CH_2-CHO$

29.

$$CH_3-\underset{\underset{\textstyle CH_3}{|}}{\overset{\overset{\textstyle CH_3}{|}}{C}}-CHO$$

30. diisopropylacetaldehyde

31.

$$CH_3-\underset{\underset{\textstyle CH_3}{|}}{\overset{\overset{\textstyle CH_3}{|}}{C}}-CH_2-\underset{\underset{\textstyle CH_3}{|}}{\overset{\overset{\textstyle CH_3}{|}}{C}}-CHO$$

2,2,4,4-tetramethylpentanal

32. diethyl ketone

33.

$$CH_3-CO-CH_2-\underset{\underset{\textstyle CH_3}{|}}{CH}-CH_3$$

methyl isobutyl ketone

34. dicyclopropyl ketone

35. $CH_3-CH_2-CO-CH_2-CH=CH_2$

β and γ
3
5
5-hexen-3-one

36. $CH_3-CO-CH=CH_2$

α and β

120

1. secondary

2. tertiary

3. $R-NH_2$
   $R-NH-R$ or R_2NH

   $R-\underset{\underset{R}{|}}{N}-R$ or R_3N

4. tertiary
   primary

5. secondary
   primary

6. primary
   primary

7. methylamine
   ethylamine

8. $CH_3-\underset{\underset{CH_3}{|}}{N}-CH_3$ or $(CH_3)_3N$

9. $CH_3-\underset{\underset{CH_3}{|}}{\overset{\overset{CH_3}{|}}{C}}-NH_2$ or $(CH_3)_3C-NH_2$

   primary

10. s-butylamine

11. 3,5-dimethyl-3-ethylhexyl
    3,5-dimethyl-3-ethylhexylamine

12. $CH_3-CH_2-CH_2-CH_2-\underset{\underset{CH_3-CH_2}{|}}{CH}-NH_2$

13.

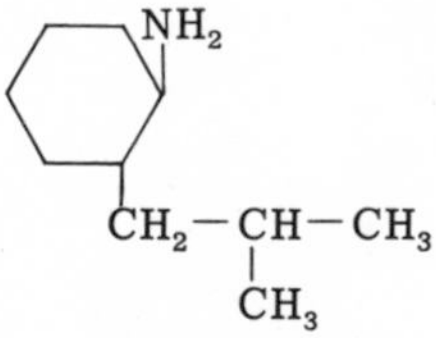

    or

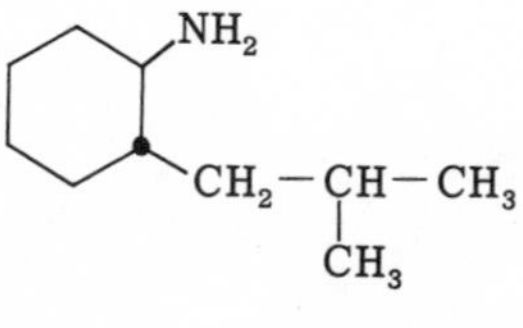

14.

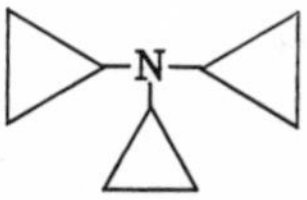

15. isobutylamine
    N-allylisobutylamine

16. N,N-dimethyldecylamine

17. $CH_2=CH-$$-N(CH_3)_2$

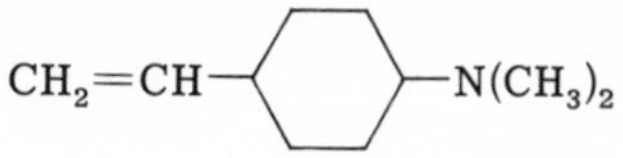

18. 1
    1 and 4
    1,4-dimethylpentylamine

19. 7
    10
    10-ethyl-7-dodecenylamine
    (or 10-ethyl-7-dodecen-1-amine)

20. 6-methoxy-3-cyclooctenylamine
    (or 6-methoxy-3-cycloocten-1-amine)

21. 1-pentenylamine
    N, 1, and 3
    N
    N,1,3-trimethyl-N-ethyl-1-pentenylamine)

22. hydroxy
    2-hydroxy-1-ethylbutylamine
    4-amino-3-hexanol

23.

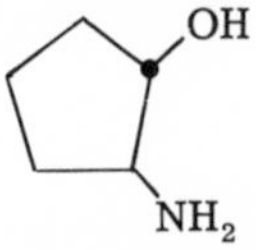

    or

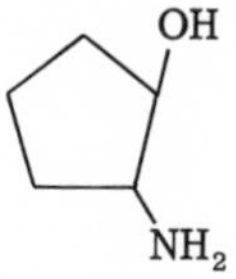

24.

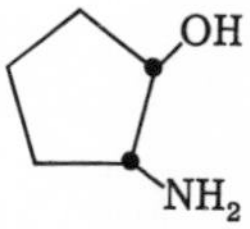

    or

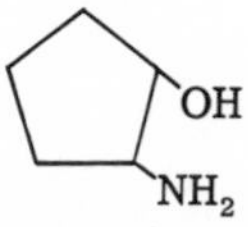

25. dimethylamino
    5
    4
    4-methyl-5-dimethylamino-2-pentanone

26. $CH_3-CH_2-CH_2-CH_2-CH_2-CH_2-CH_2-CH-CH-\overset{\displaystyle O}{\overset{\displaystyle \|}{C}}-O-CH_2-CH_3$
    $\qquad\qquad\qquad\qquad\qquad\quad CH_3-CH_2-O \quad N(CH_2-CH_3)_2$

27. 1,4-butanediamine
    1,5-pentanediamine

28. $H_2N-CH_2-CH_2-CH_2-CH_2-CH_2-CH_2-NH_2$

29. $CH_3-\underset{\underset{\displaystyle NH_2}{|}}{CH}-\overset{\overset{\displaystyle CH_3}{|}}{CH}-\underset{\underset{\displaystyle NH_2}{|}}{CH}-CH_3$

30. $H_2N-CH_2-CH_2-NH_2$

31. $H_2N-CH_2-CH_2-CH_2-CH_2-CH_2-CH_2-NH_2$
    or $H_2N-(CH_2)_6-NH_2$
    hexamethylenediamine

32. $H_2N-CH_2-CH_2-CH_2-CH_2-NH_2$
    or $H_2N-(CH_2)_4-NH_2$

33. diethylamine
    diethylammonium chloride

34. tri
    tetra
    ionic or electrovalent

35. $CH_3-\underset{\underset{\displaystyle CH_3}{|}}{CH}-NH-\underset{\underset{\displaystyle CH_3}{|}}{CH}-CH_2-CH_3$

    $CH_3-\underset{\underset{\displaystyle CH_3}{|}}{CH}-\overset{+}{N}H_2-\underset{\underset{\displaystyle CH_3}{|}}{CH}-CH_2-CH_3 \quad ClO_4^-$

36. $CH_3-CH_2-CH_2-CH_2-CH_2-\underset{\quad}{CH}-CH_2-CH_3$
    $\qquad\qquad\qquad CH_3-\underset{\underset{\displaystyle CH_3}{|}}{CH}-CH_2-\overset{+}{N}H-CH_2-CH=CH_2$
    $\qquad\qquad\qquad\qquad\qquad\qquad\qquad\quad I^-$

37. $HO-NH_2$

    $HO-\overset{+}{N}H_3 \quad Cl^-$
    hydroxylammonium chloride

38. $(CH_3)_4\overset{+}{N} \quad Cl^-$ or any other ammonium salt
    with 4 alkyl groups (all alike or different)
    bound to nitrogen

39. 12
    $CH_3-(CH_2)_{10}-CH_2-\overset{+}{N}(CH_3)_3 \quad I^-$
    quaternary ammonium

40. $CH_3-(CH_2)_{10}-CH_2-\overset{+}{N}(CH_3)_3 \quad OH^-$
    quaternary ammonium

41. $R_4\overset{+}{N} \quad OH^-$

42. tetra
    ionic or electrovalent

1. ethylbenzene

2. $H-C\equiv C-$

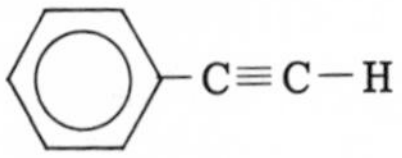

    $-C\equiv C-H$

3. $-CH-CH_2-CH_3$ / $\quad\quad CH_3$

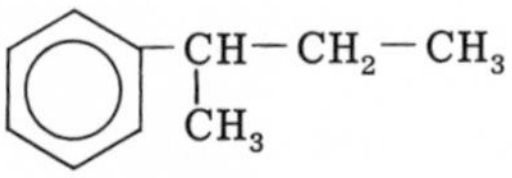

4. neopentyl
    neopentylbenzene

5. 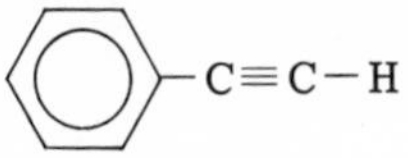 $-C\equiv C-H$

    phenylacetylene

6. 2-nonene
    4
    6
    4-methyl-6-phenyl-2-nonene

7. 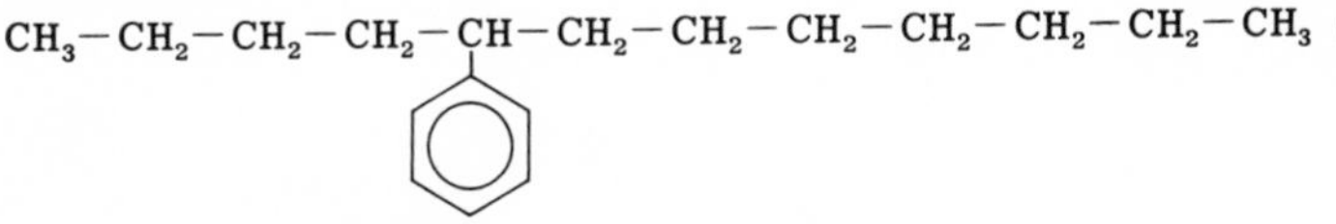 $CH_3-CH_2-CH_2-CH_2-CH-CH_2-CH_2-CH_2-CH_2-CH_2-CH_2-CH_3$ $\underline{or}$ $CH_3-(CH_2)_3-CH-(CH_2)_6-CH_3$
    ϕ

8. 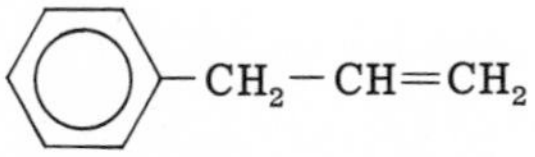 $-CH_2-CH=CH_2$

    $\underline{or}$ $C_6H_5-CH_2-CH=CH_2$

    $\underline{or}$ $\phi-CH_2-CH=CH_2$
    3-phenylpropene
    1-phenylpropene

9. 1, 3

10. 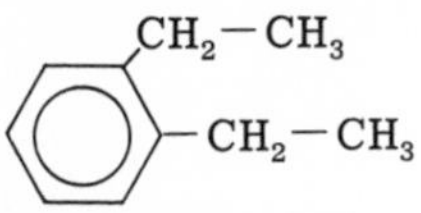 $-CH_2-CH_3$ / $-CH_2-CH_3$

11. 1, 2, 4
    1,4-dimethyl-2-isopropylbenzene

12.

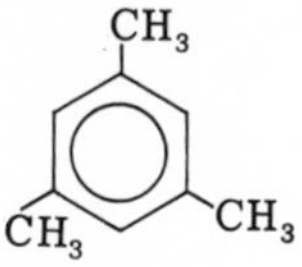

13. 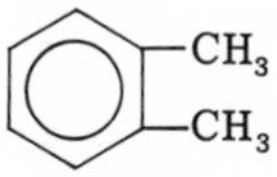 $-CH_3$ / $-CH_3$

    $CH_3-$$-CH_3$

14. p-diisopropylbenzene

15. o(ortho)

16. CH_2-CH_3 / $CH=CH_2$

17. o-isobutylhexylbenzene

18. $CH_3-$$-CH_2-CH_3$

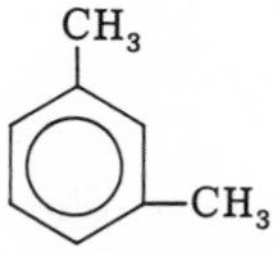

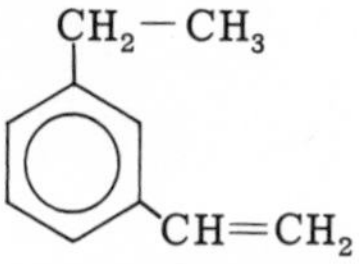

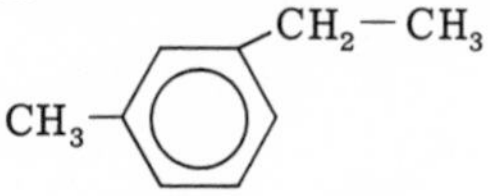

19. 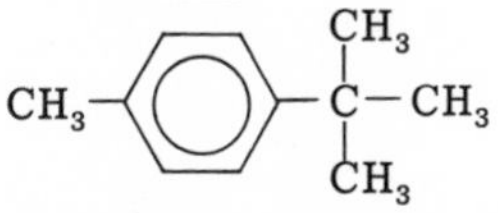 $CH_3-$$-C-CH_3$

20. 2-allyltoluene $\underline{or}$ o-allyltoluene

21. 1-methyl-4-s-butylbenzene
    4-s-butyltoluene $\underline{or}$ p-s-butyltoluene

22. $CH_2=CH-$ $\underline{or}$ $CH_2=CH-\phi$

23. $CH_2=CH-$$-CH_2-CH-CH_3$
    CH_3

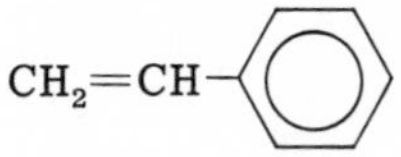

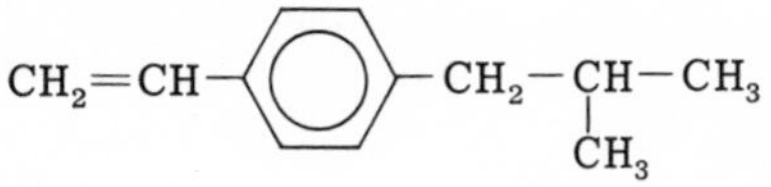

24. 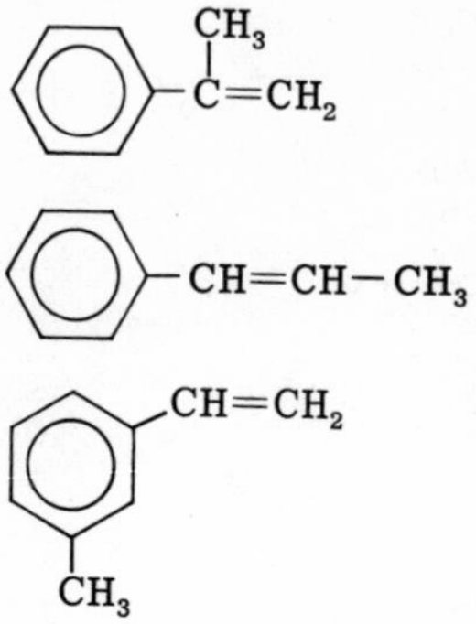
CH3
C=CH2
CH=CH−CH3
CH=CH2
CH3

25. α-propylstyrene
2-phenyl-1-pentene

1. ethylbenzene
   chlorobenzene
   nitrobenzene

2.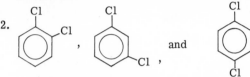

   o-dichlorobenzene, m-dichlorobenzene,
     and p-dichlorobenzene
   1,2-dichlorobenzene, 1,3-dichlorobenzene,
     and 1,4-dichlorobenzene

3.

   1-nitro-3-chlorobenzene
     or 1-chloro-3-nitrobenzene

4. 1, 2, 3, 5
   1,3,5-trinitro-2-chlorobenzene

5.

6. the use of benzene as the basis of a name
   requires the use of the smallest possible
   numbers, while the use of toluene as the
   basis of the name requires that the methyl
   group be on position number 1.

7.

   o-chlorotoluene, m-chlorotoluene, and
     p-chlorotoluene (or 2-chlorotoluene,
     3-chlorotoluene, and 4-chlorotoluene).

8. $-CH_2-Cl$

9. α-chlorotoluene

10. $-CH_2-NO_2$

11. benzyl chloride
    benzyl alcohol
    methyl benzyl ether

12. p-nitrobenzyl chloride

13. CH_2-OH
    OCH_3

14. $-MgBr$ or $\phi-MgBr$

    or C_6H_5-MgBr or $Ph-MgBr$

    $-CH_2-MgBr$ or $\phi-CH_2-MgBr$

    or $C_6H_5-CH_2-MgBr$ or $Ph-CH_2-MgBr$

15. $\phi-O-CH_2-CH=CH_2$

    or $-O-CH_2-CH=CH_2$

    $\phi-CH_2-O-CH=CH_2$

    or $-CH_2-O-CH=CH_2$

16. $-CH=CH_2$

17. $CH=CH_2$ 2-bromostyrene
    Br   or o-bromostyrene

    $CH=CH_2$ 3-bromostyrene
               or m-bromostyrene
    Br

    $CH=CH_2$ 4-bromostyrene
               or p-bromostyrene
    Br

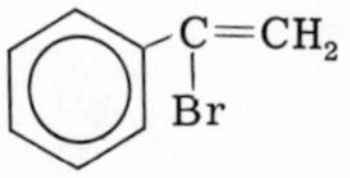

α-bromostyrene

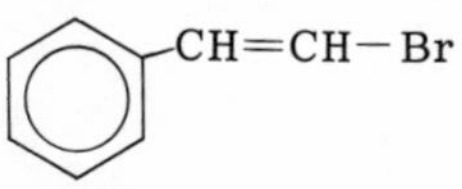

β-bromostyrene

18.

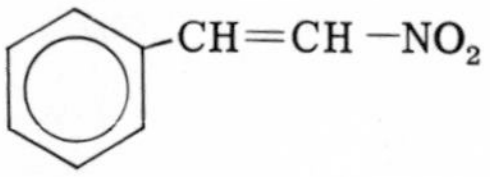

19.

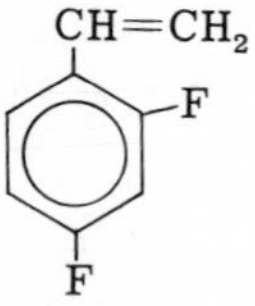

20. benzyl
    3-fluoro-4-benzylstyrene
    <u>or</u> 4-benzyl-3-fluorostyrene

21. benzenesulfonic acid

22.

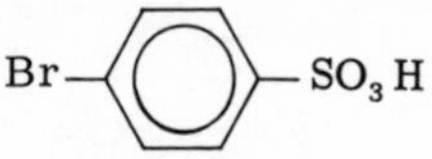

23.

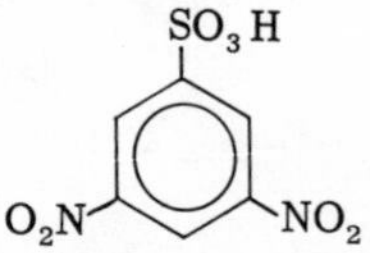

24. p-toluenesulfonic acid
    (<u>or</u> 4-toluenesulfonic acid)

25. ethyl benzenesulfonate

26.

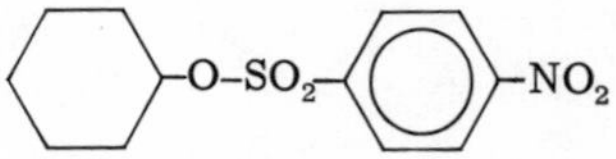

27. <u>p</u>-nitrobenzyl <u>p</u>-toluenesulfonate
    (<u>or</u> 4-nitrobenzyl 4-toluenesulfonate)

CHAPTER 13 BRIDGED RING SYSTEMS

1. 8
   bicyclooctane
2. bicyclopentane
3. 3, 2, 1
4. 2, 1, 0
5. bicyclo[2.1.0]pentane
6. bicyclo[4.2.0]octane
   bicyclo[4.1.1]octane
   bicyclo[3.3.0]octane
   bicyclo[5.1.0]octane
   bicyclo[2.2.2]octane
7. 2
   7
8. 7
   3
9. 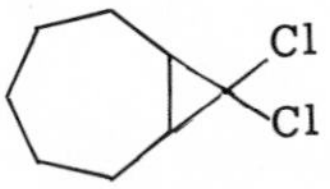

10. 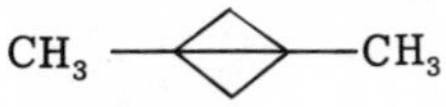

11. 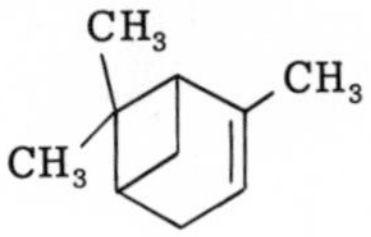

12. 3,7,7-trimethylbicyclo[4.1.0]hept-3-ene
13. bicyclo[2.2.1]hept-2-ene
14. 1,7,7-trimethylbicyclo[2.2.1]heptan-2-one
15. bicyclo[2.1.1]hexan-5-ol
16. 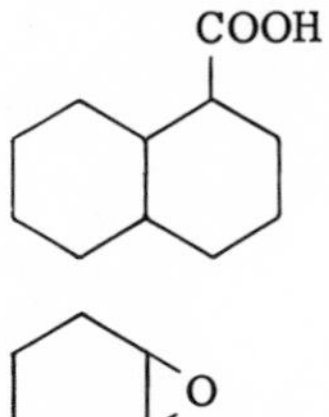

17. 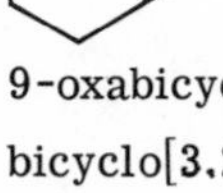

18. 9-oxabicyclo[4.2.1]nonane
19. bicyclo[3.2.2]nonane
    aza
    3-azabicyclo[3.2.2]nonane
20. 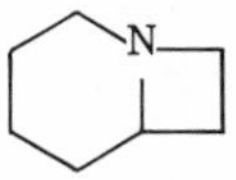

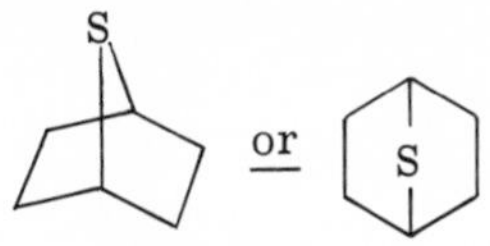

21. 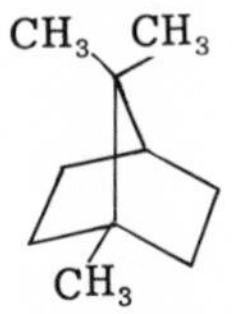

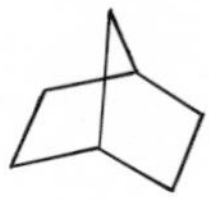

22. 2
    2-nitronorbornane
23. 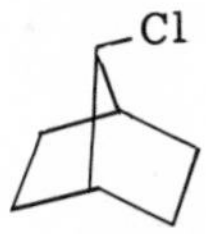

24. 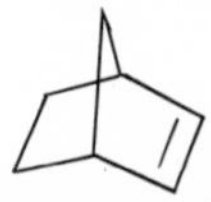

    2,5-norbornadiene
25. 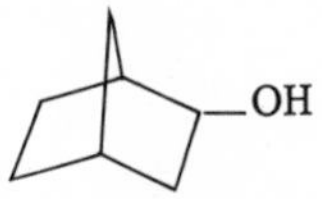

    7-norbornanol
26. 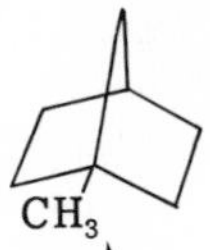

27. 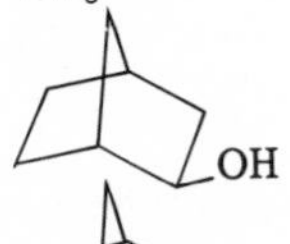

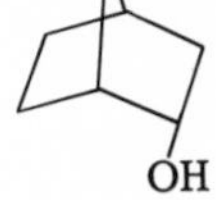

28. <u>endo</u>-2-bromonorbornane

29.

30. <u>exo</u>-2-norbornylamine

1. one
   0
   radical

2. carbonium ion

3. − charge
   carbanion
   $\overset{..}{C}H_3$(or :CH_3 or $\bar{C}H_3$)

4. isopropyl cation
      or isopropyl carbonium ion

5. t-butyl cation
      or t-butyl carbonium ion

6. $CH_3-\overset{\overset{\displaystyle CH_3}{|}}{\underset{+}{C}}-CH_2-CH_3$

7. $CH_3-\overset{+}{C}H-CH_2-CH_3$

   $CH_3-\overset{\overset{\displaystyle CH_3}{|}}{C}H-\overset{+}{C}H_2$

8. secondary
   primary

9.

   tertiary

10. radical
    isopropyl radical

11. $CH_3-\overset{\overset{\displaystyle CH_3}{|}}{\underset{\underset{\displaystyle CH_3}{|}}{C}}\cdot$

    tertiary

12. carbanion
    isobutyl anion or isobutyl carbanion

13. primary

14. $Cl_3\bar{C}$
    $Cl_3C\cdot$

15. allyl cation or allyl carbonium ion
    vinyl anion or vinyl carbanion

16. $CH_2{=}CH-\overset{.}{C}H_2$

17. $\triangleright\!\!-\overset{+}{C}H_2$

    primary

18. propyl
    1,1-diethylpropyl radical
    tertiary

19. 2

20. 0

21. 0
    2

22. chloromethylene

23. Cl_2C:
    singlet
    triplet
    an excited

24. $CH_3-\overset{\overset{\displaystyle CH_3}{|}}{\underset{\underset{\displaystyle CH_3}{|}}{C}}-\overset{..}{C}H$ or $(CH_3)_3C-\overset{..}{C}H$

    neopentyl

25. $CH_3-\overset{\overset{\displaystyle CH_3}{|}}{\underset{\underset{\displaystyle CH_3}{|}}{C}}-CH_2-\overset{..}{C}H$

    or $(CH_3)_3C-CH_2-\overset{..}{C}H$

26. di-s-butylmethylene